MW00804178

# www.EffortlessMath.com

... So Much More Online!

✓ FREE Math lessons

✓ More Math learning books!

✓ Mathematics Worksheets

✓ Online Math Tutors

**Need a PDF version of this book?**

Please visit www.EffortlessMath.com

# PSAT Math Exercise Book

## *Student Workbook and Two Realistic*

## *PSAT Math Tests*

By

Reza Nazari & Ava Ross

Copyright © 2019

Reza Nazari & Ava Ross

All rights reserved. No part of this publication may be reproduced, stored in a retrieval system, or transmitted in any form or by any means, electronic, mechanical, photocopying, recording, scanning, or otherwise, except as permitted under Section 107 or 108 of the 1976 United States Copyright Ac, without permission of the author.

All inquiries should be addressed to:

info@effortlessMath.com

www.EffortlessMath.com

**ISBN-13:** 978-1-970036-66-4

**ISBN-10:** 1-970036-66-4

**Published by: Effortless Math Education**

**www.EffortlessMath.com**

## Description

**Get ready for the PSAT Math Test with a PERFECT Math Workbook!**

*PSAT Math Exercise book*, which reflects the 2019 test guidelines and topics, is dedicated to preparing test takers to ace the PSAT Math Test. This PSAT Math workbook's new edition has been updated to replicate questions appearing on the most recent PSAT Math tests. Here is intensive preparation for the PSAT Math test, and a precious learning tool for test takers who need extra practice in math to raise their PSAT Math scores. After completing this workbook, you will have solid foundation and adequate practice that is necessary to ace the PSAT Math test. **This workbook is your ticket to score higher on PSAT Math.**

The updated version of this hands-on workbook represents extensive exercises, math problems, sample PSAT questions, and quizzes with answers and detailed solutions to help you hone your math skills, overcome your exam anxiety, and boost your confidence -- and do your best to defeat PSAT exam on test day.

Each of math exercises is answered in the book and we have provided explanation of the answers for the two full-length PSAT Math practice tests as well which will help test takers find their weak areas and raise their scores. This is a unique and perfect practice book to beat the PSAT Math Test.

Separate math chapters offer a complete review of the PSAT Math test, including:

- ✓ Arithmetic and Number Operations
- ✓ Algebra and Functions,
- ✓ Geometry and Measurement
- ✓ Data analysis, Statistics, & Probability
- ✓ ... and also includes **two full-length practice tests!**

The surest way to succeed on PSAT Math Test is with intensive practice in every math topic tested--and that's what you will get in *PSAT Math Exercise Book*. Each chapter of this focused format has a comprehensive review created by Test Prep experts that goes into detail to cover all of the content likely to appear on the PSAT Math test. Not only does this all-inclusive workbook offer everything you will ever need to conquer PSAT Math test, it also contains two full-length and realistic PSAT Math tests that reflect the format and question types on the PSAT to help you check your exam-readiness and identify where you need more practice.

*Effortless Math Workbook* for the PSAT Test contains many exciting and unique features to help you improve your test scores, including:

- ✓ Content 100% aligned with the 2019 PSAT test
- ✓ Written by PSAT Math tutors and test experts
- ✓ Complete coverage of all PSAT Math concepts and topics which you will be tested
- ✓ Over 2,500 additional PSAT math practice questions in both multiple-choice and grid-in formats with answers grouped by topic, so you can focus on your weak areas
- ✓ Abundant Math skill building exercises to help test-takers approach different question types that might be unfamiliar to them
- ✓ Exercises on different PSAT Math topics such as integers, percent, equations, polynomials, exponents and radicals
- ✓ 2 full-length practice tests (featuring new question types) with detailed answers

This PSAT Math Workbook and other Effortless Math Education books are used by thousands of students each year to help them review core content areas, brush-up in math, discover their strengths and weaknesses, and achieve their best scores on the PSAT test.

**Do NOT take the PSAT test without reviewing the Math questions in this workbook!**

## About the Author

**Reza Nazari** is the author of more than 100 Math learning books including:
– **Math and Critical Thinking Challenges:** For the Middle and High School Student
– **PSAT Math in 30 Days**
– **ASVAB Math Workbook 2018 - 2019**
– **Effortless Math Education Workbooks**
– **and many more Mathematics books ...**

Reza is also an experienced Math instructor and a test–prep expert who has been tutoring students since 2008. Reza is the founder of Effortless Math Education, a tutoring company that has helped many students raise their standardized test scores—and attend the colleges of their dreams. Reza provides an individualized custom learning plan and the personalized attention that makes a difference in how students view math.

You can contact Reza via email at:
reza@EffortlessMath.com

Find Reza's professional profile at:
goo.gl/zoC9rJ

# Contents

# Chapter 1:

# Basics

## Topics that you'll practice in this chapter:

✓ Simplifying Fractions

✓ Adding and Subtracting Fractions

✓ Multiplying and Dividing Fractions

✓ Adding and Subtract Mixed Numbers

✓ Multiplying and Dividing Mixed Numbers

✓ Adding and Subtracting Decimals

✓ Multiplying and Dividing Decimals

✓ Comparing Decimals

✓ Rounding Decimals

✓ Factoring Numbers

✓ Greatest Common Factor

✓ Least Common Multiple

*"A Man is like a fraction whose numerator is what he is and whose denominator is what he thinks of himself. The larger the denominator, the smaller the fraction." –Tolstoy*

# Simplifying Fractions

✎ *Simplify each fraction to its lowest terms.*

1) $\frac{9}{18} =$

2) $\frac{8}{10} =$

3) $\frac{6}{8} =$

4) $\frac{5}{20} =$

5) $\frac{18}{24} =$

6) $\frac{6}{9} =$

7) $\frac{12}{15} =$

8) $\frac{4}{16} =$

9) $\frac{18}{36} =$

10) $\frac{6}{42} =$

11) $\frac{13}{39} =$

12) $\frac{21}{28} =$

13) $\frac{63}{77} =$

14) $\frac{36}{40} =$

15) $\frac{21}{63} =$

16) $\frac{30}{84} =$

17) $\frac{50}{125} =$

18) $\frac{72}{108} =$

19) $\frac{49}{112} =$

20) $\frac{240}{320} =$

21) $\frac{120}{150} =$

✎ *Solve each problem.*

22) Which of the following fractions equal to $\frac{4}{5}$? _____

A. $\frac{64}{75}$        B. $\frac{92}{115}$        C. $\frac{60}{85}$        D. $\frac{160}{220}$

23) Which of the following fractions equal to $\frac{3}{7}$? _____

A. $\frac{63}{147}$        B. $\frac{75}{182}$        C. $\frac{54}{140}$        D. $\frac{39}{98}$

24) Which of the following fractions equal to $\frac{2}{9}$? _____

A. $\frac{84}{386}$        B. $\frac{52}{234}$        C. $\frac{96}{450}$        D. $\frac{112}{522}$

# Adding and Subtracting Fractions

✍ **Find the sum.**

1) $\frac{1}{3} + \frac{2}{3} =$

2) $\frac{1}{2} + \frac{1}{3} =$

3) $\frac{2}{5} + \frac{1}{2} =$

4) $\frac{3}{7} + \frac{2}{3} =$

5) $\frac{3}{4} + \frac{2}{5} =$

6) $\frac{3}{5} + \frac{1}{5} =$

7) $\frac{5}{9} + \frac{1}{2} =$

8) $\frac{3}{5} + \frac{3}{8} =$

9) $\frac{5}{9} + \frac{3}{7} =$

10) $\frac{5}{11} + \frac{1}{4} =$

11) $\frac{3}{7} + \frac{1}{6} =$

12) $\frac{3}{14} + \frac{3}{4} =$

✍ **Find the difference.**

13) $\frac{1}{2} - \frac{1}{3} =$

14) $\frac{4}{5} - \frac{2}{3} =$

15) $\frac{2}{3} - \frac{1}{6} =$

16) $\frac{3}{5} - \frac{1}{2} =$

17) $\frac{8}{9} - \frac{2}{5} =$

18) $\frac{4}{7} - \frac{1}{9} =$

19) $\frac{2}{5} - \frac{1}{4} =$

20) $\frac{5}{8} - \frac{2}{6} =$

21) $\frac{4}{15} - \frac{1}{10} =$

22) $\frac{7}{20} - \frac{1}{5} =$

23) $\frac{3}{18} - \frac{1}{12} =$

24) $\frac{9}{24} - \frac{3}{16} =$

25) $\frac{3}{7} - \frac{2}{5} =$

26) $\frac{5}{9} - \frac{1}{6} =$

27) $\frac{2}{5} - \frac{1}{10} =$

28) $\frac{5}{12} - \frac{2}{9} =$

29) $\frac{2}{13} - \frac{3}{7} =$

30) $\frac{4}{11} - \frac{5}{8} =$

# Multiplying and Dividing Fractions

✏️ **Find the value of each expression in lowest terms.**

1) $\frac{1}{2} \times \frac{3}{4} =$

2) $\frac{3}{5} \times \frac{2}{3} =$

3) $\frac{1}{4} \times \frac{2}{5} =$

4) $\frac{1}{6} \times \frac{4}{5} =$

5) $\frac{1}{5} \times \frac{1}{4} =$

6) $\frac{2}{5} \times \frac{1}{2} =$

7) $\frac{7}{9} \times \frac{1}{3} =$

8) $\frac{5}{7} \times \frac{3}{8} =$

9) $\frac{8}{9} \times \frac{6}{7} =$

10) $\frac{5}{6} \times \frac{3}{5} =$

11) $\frac{3}{8} \times \frac{1}{9} =$

12) $\frac{1}{12} \times \frac{3}{7} =$

✏️ **Find the value of each expression in lowest terms.**

13) $\frac{1}{2} \div \frac{1}{4} =$

14) $\frac{1}{3} \div \frac{1}{2} =$

15) $\frac{2}{5} \div \frac{1}{3} =$

16) $\frac{1}{4} \div \frac{2}{3} =$

17) $\frac{1}{5} \div \frac{3}{10} =$

18) $\frac{2}{7} \div \frac{1}{3} =$

19) $\frac{3}{5} \div \frac{5}{9} =$

20) $\frac{2}{23} \div \frac{2}{9} =$

21) $\frac{4}{13} \div \frac{1}{4} =$

22) $\frac{9}{14} \div \frac{3}{7} =$

23) $\frac{8}{15} \div \frac{2}{5} =$

24) $\frac{2}{9} \div \frac{7}{11} =$

25) $\frac{2}{5} \div \frac{3}{4} =$

26) $\frac{4}{11} \div \frac{2}{5} =$

27) $\frac{2}{15} \div \frac{5}{8} =$

28) $\frac{3}{10} \div \frac{2}{5} =$

29) $\frac{4}{5} \div \frac{3}{7} =$

30) $\frac{2}{11} \div \frac{3}{5} =$

# Adding and Subtracting Mixed Numbers

✎ **Find the sum.**

1) $2\frac{1}{2} + 1\frac{1}{3} =$

2) $6\frac{1}{2} + 3\frac{1}{2} =$

3) $2\frac{3}{8} + 3\frac{1}{8} =$

4) $4\frac{1}{2} + 1\frac{1}{4} =$

5) $1\frac{3}{7} + 1\frac{5}{14} =$

6) $6\frac{5}{12} + 3\frac{3}{4} =$

7) $5\frac{1}{2} + 8\frac{3}{4} =$

8) $3\frac{7}{8} + 3\frac{1}{3} =$

9) $3\frac{3}{9} + 7\frac{6}{11} =$

10) $7\frac{5}{12} + 4\frac{3}{10} =$

✎ **Find the difference.**

11) $3\frac{1}{3} - 1\frac{1}{3} =$

12) $4\frac{1}{2} - 3\frac{1}{2} =$

13) $5\frac{1}{2} - 2\frac{1}{4} =$

14) $6\frac{1}{6} - 5\frac{1}{3} =$

15) $8\frac{1}{2} - 1\frac{1}{10} =$

16) $9\frac{1}{2} - 2\frac{1}{4} =$

17) $9\frac{1}{5} - 5\frac{1}{6} =$

18) $14\frac{3}{10} - 13\frac{1}{3} =$

19) $19\frac{2}{3} - 11\frac{5}{8} =$

20) $20\frac{3}{4} - 14\frac{2}{3} =$

21) $2\frac{1}{2} - 1\frac{1}{5} =$

22) $3\frac{1}{6} - 1\frac{1}{10} =$

23) $16\frac{2}{7} - 11\frac{2}{3} =$

24) $15\frac{1}{7} - 10\frac{1}{8} =$

25) $12\frac{3}{4} - 7\frac{1}{3} =$

26) $15\frac{2}{5} - 5\frac{2}{3} =$

# *Multiplying and Dividing Mixed Numbers*

✎ **Find the product.**

1) $4\frac{1}{3} \times 2\frac{1}{5} =$

2) $3\frac{1}{2} \times 3\frac{1}{4} =$

3) $5\frac{2}{5} \times 2\frac{1}{3} =$

4) $2\frac{1}{2} \times 1\frac{2}{9} =$

5) $3\frac{4}{7} \times 2\frac{3}{5} =$

6) $7\frac{2}{3} \times 2\frac{2}{3} =$

7) $9\frac{8}{9} \times 8\frac{3}{4} =$

8) $2\frac{4}{7} \times 5\frac{2}{9} =$

9) $5\frac{2}{5} \times 2\frac{3}{5} =$

10) $3\frac{5}{7} \times 3\frac{5}{6} =$

✎ **Find the quotient.**

11) $1\frac{2}{3} \div 3\frac{1}{3} =$

12) $2\frac{1}{4} \div 1\frac{1}{2} =$

13) $10\frac{1}{2} \div 1\frac{2}{3} =$

14) $3\frac{1}{6} \div 4\frac{2}{3} =$

15) $4\frac{1}{8} \div 2\frac{1}{2} =$

16) $2\frac{1}{10} \div 2\frac{3}{5} =$

17) $1\frac{4}{11} \div 1\frac{1}{4} =$

18) $9\frac{1}{2} \div 9\frac{2}{3} =$

19) $8\frac{3}{4} \div 2\frac{2}{5} =$

20) $12\frac{1}{2} \div 9\frac{1}{3} =$

21) $2\frac{1}{8} \div 1\frac{1}{2} =$

22) $1\frac{1}{10} \div 1\frac{3}{5} =$

23) $5\frac{2}{5} \div 1\frac{3}{4} =$

24) $5\frac{1}{2} \div 2\frac{2}{3} =$

25) $3\frac{3}{4} \div 1\frac{1}{5} =$

26) $3\frac{1}{2} \div 1\frac{1}{3} =$

# Adding and Subtracting Decimals

✎ **Add and subtract decimals.**

1) $\begin{array}{r} 31.13 \\ -\ 11.45 \\ \hline \phantom{00000} \end{array}$

4) $\begin{array}{r} 56.67 \\ -\ 44.39 \\ \hline \phantom{00000} \end{array}$

7) $\begin{array}{r} 66.24 \\ -\ 23.11 \\ \hline \phantom{00000} \end{array}$

2) $\begin{array}{r} 35.25 \\ +\ 24.47 \\ \hline \phantom{00000} \end{array}$

5) $\begin{array}{r} 71.47 \\ +\ 16.25 \\ \hline \phantom{00000} \end{array}$

8) $\begin{array}{r} 39.75 \\ +\ 12.85 \\ \hline \phantom{00000} \end{array}$

3) $\begin{array}{r} 73.50 \\ +\ 22.78 \\ \hline \phantom{00000} \end{array}$

6) $\begin{array}{r} 68.99 \\ -\ 53.61 \\ \hline \phantom{00000} \end{array}$

9) $\begin{array}{r} 229.25 \\ -\ 84.67 \\ \hline \phantom{00000} \end{array}$

✎ **Find the missing number.**

10) ___ $+\ 2.5 = 3.9$

11) $1.7 +$ ___ $= 4.98$

12) $5.25 +$ ___ $= 7$

13) $6.55 -$ ___ $= 2.45$

14) ___ $-\ 3.98 = 5.32$

15) ___ $-\ 11.67 = 14.48$

16) $12.35 +$ ___ $= 14.78$

17) ___ $-\ 23.89 = 13.90$

18) ___ $+\ 17.28 = 19.56$

19) $77.90 +$ ___ $= 102.60$

# *Multiplying and Dividing Decimals*

✍ **Find the product.**

1) $0.5 \times 0.4 =$

2) $2.5 \times 0.2 =$

3) $1.25 \times 0.5 =$

4) $0.75 \times 0.2 =$

5) $1.92 \times 0.8 =$

6) $0.55 \times 0.4 =$

7) $3.24 \times 1.2 =$

8) $12.5 \times 4.2 =$

9) $22.6 \times 8.2 =$

10) $17.2 \times 4.5 =$

11) $25.1 \times 12.5 =$

12) $33.2 \times 2.2 =$

✍ **Find the quotient.**

13) $1.67 \div 100 =$

14) $52.2 \div 1,000 =$

15) $4.2 \div 2 =$

16) $8.6 \div 0.5 =$

17) $12.6 \div 0.2 =$

18) $16.5 \div 5 =$

19) $13.25 \div 100 =$

20) $25.6 \div 0.4 =$

21) $28.24 \div 0.1 =$

22) $34.16 \div 0.25 =$

23) $44.28 \div 0.5 =$

24) $38.78 \div 0.02 =$

# Comparing Decimals

✍ *Write the correct comparison symbol (>, < or =).*

1)  0.50 ☐ 0.050

2) 0.025 ☐ 0.25

3) 2.060 ☐ 2.07

4) 1.75 ☐ 1.07

5) 4.04 ☐ 0.440

6) 3.05 ☐ 3.5

7) 5.05 ☐ 5.050

8) 1.02 ☐ 1.1

9) 2.45 ☐ 2.125

10) 0.932 ☐ 0.0932

11) 3.15 ☐ 3.150

12) 0.718 ☐ 0.89

13) 7.060 ☐ 7.60

14) 3.59 ☐ 3.129

15) 4.33 ☐ 4.319

16) 2.25 ☐ 2.250

17) 1.95 ☐ 1.095

18) 8.051 ☐ 8.50

19) 1.022 ☐ 1.020

20) 3.77 ☐ 3.770

# *Rounding Decimals*

✎ *Round each decimal to the nearest whole number.*

1) 23.18          3) 14.45          5) 3.95

2) 8.6            4) 7.5            6) 56.7

✎ *Round each decimal to the nearest tenth.*

7) 22.652         9) 47.847         11) 16.184

8) 30.342         10) 82.88         12) 71.79

✎ *Round each decimal to the nearest hundredth.*

13) 5.439         15) 26.1855       17) 91.448

14) 12.907        16) 48.623        18) 29.354

✎ *Round each decimal to the nearest thousandth.*

19) 14.67374      21) 78.7191       23) 10.0678

20) 7.54647       22) 70.2732       24) 46.54765

# Factoring Numbers

✎ *List all positive factors of each number.*

1) 8

2) 9

3) 15

4) 16

5) 25

6) 28

7) 26

8) 35

9) 42

10) 48

11) 50

12) 36

13) 55

14) 40

15) 62

16) 84

17) 75

18) 68

19) 96

20) 78

21) 94

22) 82

23) 81

24) 72

# Greatest Common Factor

✍ *Find the GCF for each number pair.*

1) 4, 2

2) 3, 5

3) 2, 6

4) 4, 7

5) 5, 10

6) 6, 12

7) 7, 14

8) 6, 14

9) 5, 12

10) 4, 14

11) 15, 18

12) 12, 20

13) 12, 16

14) 15, 27

15) 8, 24

16) 28, 16

17) 32, 24

18) 18, 36

19) 26, 20

20) 30, 14

21) 24, 20

22) 14, 22

23) 25, 15

24) 28, 32

# *Least Common Multiple*

✎ *Find the LCM for each number pair.*

1) 3, 6

2) 5, 10

3) 6, 14

4) 8, 9

5) 6, 18

6) 10, 12

7) 4, 12

8) 5, 15

9) 4, 18

10) 9, 12

11) 12, 16

12) 15, 18

13) 8, 24

14) 9, 28

15) 12, 24

16) 15, 20

17) 25, 18

18) 27, 24

19) 28, 18

20) 16, 30

21) 14, 28

22) 20, 35

23) 25, 30

24) 32, 27

# *Answers of Worksheets – Chapter 1*

## *Simplifying Fractions*

1) $\frac{1}{2}$

2) $\frac{4}{5}$

3) $\frac{3}{4}$

4) $\frac{1}{4}$

5) $\frac{3}{4}$

6) $\frac{2}{3}$

7) $\frac{4}{5}$

8) $\frac{1}{4}$

9) $\frac{1}{2}$

10) $\frac{1}{7}$

11) $\frac{1}{3}$

12) $\frac{3}{4}$

13) $\frac{9}{11}$

14) $\frac{9}{10}$

15) $\frac{1}{3}$

16) $\frac{5}{14}$

17) $\frac{2}{5}$

18) $\frac{2}{3}$

19) $\frac{7}{16}$

20) $\frac{3}{4}$

21) $\frac{4}{5}$

22) B

23) A

24) B

## *Adding and Subtracting Fractions*

1) $\frac{3}{3} = 1$

2) $\frac{5}{6}$

3) $\frac{9}{10}$

4) $\frac{23}{21}$

5) $\frac{23}{20}$

6) $\frac{4}{5}$

7) $\frac{19}{18}$

8) $\frac{39}{40}$

9) $\frac{62}{63}$

10) $\frac{31}{44}$

11) $\frac{25}{42}$

12) $\frac{27}{28}$

13) $\frac{1}{6}$

14) $\frac{2}{15}$

15) $\frac{1}{2}$

16) $\frac{1}{10}$

17) $\frac{22}{45}$

18) $\frac{29}{63}$

19) $\frac{3}{20}$

20) $\frac{7}{24}$

21) $\frac{1}{6}$

22) $\frac{3}{20}$

23) $\frac{1}{12}$

24) $\frac{3}{16}$

25) $\frac{1}{35}$

26) $\frac{7}{18}$

27) $\frac{3}{10}$

28) $\frac{7}{36}$

29) $-\frac{25}{91}$

30) $-\frac{15}{88}$

## *Multiplying and Dividing Fractions*

1) $\frac{3}{8}$

2) $\frac{2}{5}$

3) $\frac{1}{10}$

4) $\frac{2}{15}$

5) $\frac{1}{20}$

6) $\frac{1}{5}$

7) $\frac{7}{27}$

8) $\frac{15}{56}$

9) $\frac{16}{21}$

10) $\frac{1}{2}$

11) $\frac{1}{24}$

12) $\frac{1}{28}$

13) 2

14) $\frac{2}{3}$

15) $\frac{6}{5}$

16) $\frac{3}{8}$

17) $\frac{2}{3}$

18) $\frac{6}{7}$

19) $\frac{27}{25}$

20) $\frac{9}{23}$

21) $\frac{16}{13}$

22) $\frac{21}{14}$

23) $\frac{4}{3}$

24) $\frac{22}{63}$

25) $\frac{8}{15}$

26) $\frac{10}{11}$

27) $\frac{16}{75}$

28) $\frac{3}{4}$

29) $\frac{28}{15}$

30) $\frac{10}{33}$

## Adding and Subtracting Mixed Numbers

1) $3\frac{5}{6}$

2) $10$

3) $5\frac{1}{2}$

4) $5\frac{3}{4}$

5) $2\frac{11}{14}$

6) $10\frac{1}{6}$

7) $14\frac{1}{4}$

8) $7\frac{5}{24}$

9) $10\frac{29}{33}$

10) $11\frac{43}{60}$

11) $2$

12) $1$

13) $3\frac{1}{4}$

14) $\frac{5}{6}$

15) $7\frac{2}{5}$

16) $7\frac{1}{4}$

17) $4\frac{1}{30}$

18) $\frac{29}{30}$

19) $8\frac{1}{24}$

20) $6\frac{1}{12}$

21) $\frac{13}{10}$

22) $2\frac{1}{15}$

23) $4\frac{13}{21}$

24) $5\frac{1}{56}$

25) $5\frac{5}{12}$

26) $9\frac{11}{15}$

## Multiplying and Dividing Mixed Numbers

1) $9\frac{8}{15}$

2) $11\frac{3}{8}$

3) $12\frac{3}{5}$

4) $3\frac{1}{18}$

5) $9\frac{2}{7}$

6) $20\frac{4}{9}$

7) $86\frac{19}{36}$

8) $13\frac{3}{7}$

9) $14\frac{1}{25}$

10) $14\frac{5}{21}$

11) $\frac{1}{2}$

12) $1\frac{1}{2}$

13) $6\frac{3}{10}$

14) $\frac{19}{28}$

15) $1\frac{13}{20}$

16) $\frac{21}{26}$

17) $1\frac{1}{11}$

18) $\frac{57}{58}$

19) $3\frac{31}{48}$

20) $1\frac{19}{56}$

21) $1\frac{5}{12}$

22) $\frac{11}{16}$

23) $3\frac{3}{35}$

24) $2\frac{1}{16}$

25) $3\frac{1}{8}$

26) $2\frac{5}{8}$

## Adding and Subtracting Decimals

1) 19.68
2) 59.72
3) 96.28
4) 12.28
5) 87.72
6) 15.38
7) 43.13
8) 52.60
9) 144.58
10) 1.4
11) 3.28
12) 1.75
13) 4.1
14) 9.3
15) 26.15
16) 2.43
17) 37.79
18) 2.28
19) 24.7

## Multiplying and Dividing Decimals

1) 0.2
2) 0.5
3) 0.625
4) 0.15
5) 1.536
6) 0.22
7) 3.888
8) 52.5
9) 185.32
10) 77.4
11) 313.75
12) 73.04
13) 0.0167
14) 0.0522
15) 2.1
16) 4.3
17) 63
18) 3.3
19) 0.1325
20) 64
21) 282.4
22) 136.64
23) 88.56
24) 1,939

## Comparing Decimals

1) >
2) <
3) <
4) >
5) >
6) <
7) =
8) <
9) >
10) >
11) =
12) <
13) <
14) >
15) >
16) =
17) >
18) <
19) >
20) =

## Rounding Decimals

1) 23
2) 9
3) 14
4) 8
5) 4
6) 57
7) 22.7
8) 30.3
9) 47.8
10) 82.9
11) 16.2
12) 71.8
13) 5.44
14) 12.91
15) 26.19
16) 48.62
17) 91.45
18) 29.35
19) 14.674
20) 7.546
21) 78.719
22) 70.273
23) 10.068
24) 46.548

## Factoring Numbers

1) 1, 2, 4, 8
2) 1, 3, 9
3) 1, 3, 5, 15
4) 1, 2, 4, 8, 16
5) 1, 5, 25
6) 1, 2, 4, 7, 14, 28
7) 1, 2, 13, 26
8) 1, 5, 7, 35
9) 1, 2, 3, 6, 7, 14, 21, 42
10) 1, 2, 3, 4, 6, 8, 12, 16, 24, 48
11) 1, 2, 5, 10, 25, 50
12) 1, 2, 3, 4, 6, 9, 12, 18, 36
13) 1, 5, 11, 55
14) 1, 2, 4, 5, 8, 10, 20, 40
15) 1, 2, 31, 62
16) 1, 2, 3, 4, 6, 7, 12, 14, 21, 28, 42, 84
17) 1, 3, 5, 15, 25, 75
18) 1, 2, 4, 17, 34, 68
19) 1, 2, 3, 4, 6, 8, 12, 16, 24, 32, 48, 96
20) 1, 2, 3, 6, 13, 26, 39, 78
21) 1, 2, 47, 94
22) 1, 2, 41, 82
23) 1, 3, 9, 27, 81
24) 1, 2, 3, 4, 6, 8, 9, 12, 18, 24, 36, 72

## Greatest Common Factor

1) 2
2) 1
3) 2
4) 1
5) 5
6) 6
7) 7
8) 2
9) 1
10) 2
11) 3
12) 4
13) 4
14) 3
15) 8
16) 4
17) 8
18) 18
19) 2
20) 2
21) 4
22) 2
23) 5
24) 4

## Least Common Multiple

1) 6
2) 10
3) 42
4) 72
5) 18
6) 60
7) 12
8) 15
9) 36
10) 36
11) 48
12) 90
13) 24
14) 252
15) 24
16) 60
17) 450
18) 216
19) 252
20) 240
21) 28
22) 140
23) 150
24) 864

# Chapter 2:

# Real Numbers and Integers

**Topics that you'll practice in this chapter:**

✓ Adding and Subtracting Integers

✓ Multiplying and Dividing Integers

✓ Order of Operations

✓ Ordering Integers and Numbers

✓ Integers and Absolute Value

*"If people do not believe that mathematics is simple, it is only because they do not realize how complicated life is." — John von Neumann*

# *Adding and Subtracting Integers*

✎ *Find each sum.*

1) $12 + (-5) =$

2) $(-14) + (-18) =$

3) $8 + (-28) =$

4) $43 + (-12) =$

5) $(-7) + (-11) + 4 =$

6) $37 + (-16) + 12 =$

7) $29 + (-21) + (-12) + 20 =$

8) $(-15) + (-25) + 18 + 25 =$

9) $30 + (-28) + (35 - 32) =$

10) $25 + (-15) + (44 - 17) =$

✎ *Find each difference.*

11) $(-12) - (-8) =$

12) $15 - (-20) =$

13) $(-11) - 25 =$

14) $30 - (-16) =$

15) $56 - (45 - 23) =$

16) $15 - (-4) - (-34) =$

17) $(24 + 14) - (-55) =$

18) $23 - 15 - (-3) =$

19) $49 - (15 + 12) - (-4) =$

20) $29 - (-17) - (-25) =$

21) $12 - (-8) - (-18) =$

22) $(15 - 28) - (-22) =$

23) $19 - 44 - (-14) =$

24) $67 - (57 + 19) - (-8) =$

25) $56 - (-12) + (-19) =$

26) $22 - (-44) + (-55) =$

# Multiplying and Dividing Integers

✎ **Find each product.**

1) $(-7) \times (-8) =$

2) $(-4) \times 5 =$

3) $5 \times (-11) =$

4) $(-5) \times (-20) =$

5) $-(2) \times (-8) \times 3 =$

6) $(12 - 4) \times (-10) =$

7) $14 \times (-10) \times (-5) =$

8) $(18 + 12) \times (-8) =$

9) $9 \times (-15 + 6) \times 3 =$

10) $(-5) \times (-8) \times (-12) =$

✎ **Find each quotient.**

11) $16 \div (-4) =$

12) $(-25) \div (-5) =$

13) $(-40) \div (-8) =$

14) $64 \div (-8) =$

15) $(-49) \div 7 =$

16) $(-112) \div (-4) =$

17) $168 \div (-12) =$

18) $(-121) \div (-11) =$

19) $216 \div (-12) =$

20) $-(152) \div (8) =$

21) $(-152) \div (-8) =$

22) $-216 \div (-12) =$

23) $(-198) \div (-9) =$

24) $195 \div (-13) =$

25) $-(182) \div (-7) =$

26) $(126) \div (-14) =$

# Order of Operations

✎ *Evaluate each expression.*

1) $5 + (4 \times 2) =$

2) $13 - (2 \times 5) =$

3) $(16 \times 2) + 18 =$

4) $(12 - 5) - (4 \times 3) =$

5) $25 + (14 \div 2) =$

6) $(18 \times 5) \div 5 =$

7) $(48 \div 2) \times (-4) =$

8) $(7 \times 5) + (25 - 12) =$

9) $64 + (3 \times 2) + 8 =$

10) $(20 \times 5) \div (4 + 1) =$

11) $(-9) + (12 \times 6) + 15 =$

12) $(7 \times 8) - (56 \div 4) =$

13) $(4 \times 8 \div 2) - (17 + 11) =$

14) $(18 + 8 - 15) \times 5 - 3 =$

15) $(25 - 12 + 45) \times (95 \div 5) =$

16) $28 + \left(15 - (32 \div 2)\right) =$

17) $(6 + 7 - 4 - 9) + (18 \div 2) =$

18) $(95 - 17) + (10 - 25 + 9) =$

19) $(18 \times 2) + (15 \times 5) - 12 =$

20) $12 + 8 - (42 \times 4) + 50 =$

# Ordering Integers and Numbers

✍ **Order each set of integers from least to greatest.**

1) $7, -9, -6, -1, 3$          ___, ___, ___, ___, ___, ___

2) $-4, -11, 5, 12, 9$          ___, ___, ___, ___, ___, ___

3) $18, -12, -19, 21, -20$          ___, ___, ___, ___, ___, ___

4) $-15, -25, 18, -7, 32$          ___, ___, ___, ___, ___, ___

5) $37, -42, 28, -11, 34$          ___, ___, ___, ___, ___, ___

6) $78, 46, -19, 77, -24$          ___, ___, ___, ___, ___, ___

✍ **Order each set of integers from greatest to least.**

7) $11, 16, -9, -12, -4$          ___, ___, ___, ___, ___, ___

8) $23, 31, -14, -20, 39$          ___, ___, ___, ___, ___, ___

9) $45, -21, -18, 55, -5$          ___, ___, ___, ___, ___, ___

10) $68, 81, -14, -10, 94$          ___, ___, ___, ___, ___, ___

11) $-5, 69, -12, -43, 34$          ___, ___, ___, ___, ___, ___

12) $-56, -25, -30, 18, 29$          ___, ___, ___, ___, ___, ___

# Integers and Absolute Value

✎ *Write absolute value of each number.*

1) $|-7| =$

2) $|-11| =$

3) $|-9| =$

4) $|8| =$

5) $|4| =$

6) $|-18| =$

7) $|6| =$

8) $|0| =$

9) $|16| =$

10) $|-2| =$

11) $|-12|$

12) $|10| =$

13) $|3| =$

14) $|7| =$

15) $|-15| =$

16) $|-13| =$

17) $|19| =$

18) $|-12| =$

19) $|4| =$

20) $|-25| =$

✎ *Evaluate the value.*

21) $|-2| - \frac{|-10|}{2} =$

22) $8 - |2 - 14| - |-2| =$

23) $\frac{|-36|}{6} \times |-6| =$

24) $\frac{|5 \times -3|}{5} \times \frac{|-20|}{4} =$

25) $|2 \times -4| + \frac{|-40|}{5} =$

26) $\frac{|-28|}{4} \times \frac{|-55|}{11} =$

27) $|-12 + 4| \times \frac{|-4 \times 5|}{2}$

28) $\frac{|-10 \times 3|}{2} \times |-12| =$

# *Answers of Worksheets – Chapter 2*

## *Adding and Subtracting Integers*

1) 7
2) −32
3) −20
4) 31
5) −14
6) 33
7) 16
8) 3
9) 5

10) 37
11) −4
12) 35
13) −36
14) 46
15) 34
16) 53
17) 93
18) 11

19) 26
20) 71
21) 38
22) 9
23) −11
24) −1
25) 49
26) 11

## *Multiplying and Dividing Integers*

1) 56
2) −20
3) −55
4) 100
5) 48
6) −80
7) 700
8) −240
9) −243

10) −480
11) −4
12) 5
13) 5
14) −8
15) −7
16) 28
17) −14
18) 11

19) −18
20) −19
21) 19
22) 18
23) 22
24) −15
25) 26
26) −9

## *Order of Operations*

1) 13
2) 3
3) 50
4) −5
5) 32
6) 18
7) −96

8) 48
9) 78
10) 20
11) 78
12) 42
13) −12
14) 52

15) 1,102
16) 27
17) 9
18) 72
19) 99
20) −98

## *Ordering Integers and Numbers*

1) −9, −6, −1, 3, 7
2) −11, −4, 5, 9, 12
3) −20, −19, −12, 18, 21

4) −25, −15, −7, 18, 32
5) −42, −11, 28, 34, 37
6) −24, −19, 46, 77, 78

7)  $16, 11, -4, -9, -12$

8)  $39, 31, 23, -14, -20$

9)  $55, 45, -5, -18, -21$

10) $94, 81, 68, -10, -14$

11) $69, 34, -5, -12, -43$

12) $29, 18, -25, -30, -56$

## *Integers and Absolute Value*

1)  7

2)  11

3)  9

4)  8

5)  4

6)  18

7)  6

8)  0

9)  16

10) 2

11) 12

12) 10

13) 3

14) 7

15) 15

16) 13

17) 19

18) 12

19) 4

20) 25

21) $-3$

22) $-6$

23) 36

24) 15

25) 16

26) 35

27) 80

28) 180

# Chapter 3:

# Proportions, Ratios, and Percent

**Topics that you'll practice in this chapter:**

✓ Simplifying Ratios

✓ Proportional Ratios

✓ Similarity and Ratios

✓ Ratio and Rates Word Problems

✓ Percentage Calculations

✓ Percent Problems

✓ Discount, Tax and Tip

✓ Percent of Change

✓ Simple Interest

*Without mathematics, there's nothing you can do. Everything around you is mathematics. Everything around you is numbers." – Shakuntala Devi*

# Simplifying Ratios

✍ *Reduce each ratio.*

1) $12:8 =$ ___ : ___     9) $10:50 =$ ___ : ___     17) $21:27 =$ ___ : ___

2) $2:20 =$ ___ : ___     10) $14:18 =$ ___ : ___     18) $52:82 =$ ___ : ___

3) $3:36 =$ ___ : ___     11) $45:27 =$ ___ : ___     19) $12:36 =$ ___ : ___

4) $8:16 =$ ___ : ___     12) $49:21 =$ ___ : ___     20) $24:3 =$ ___ : ___

5) $6:100 =$ ___ : ___     13) $100:10 =$ ___ : ___     21) $15:30 =$ ___ : ___

6) $10:60 =$ ___ : ___     14) $35:45 =$ ___ : ___     22) $14:63 =$ ___ : ___

7) $21:49 =$ ___ : ___     15) $8:20 =$ ___ : ___     23) $68:80 =$ ___ : ___

8) $20:40 =$ ___ : ___     16) $25:35 =$ ___ : ___     24) $8:80 =$ ___ : ___

✍ *Write each ratio as a fraction in simplest form.*

25) $2:4 =$     32) $6:40 =$     39) $12:180 =$

26) $6:20 =$     33) $15:36 =$     40) $36:108 =$

27) $5:35 =$     34) $18:82 =$     41) $24:42 =$

28) $10:55 =$     35) $22:26 =$     42) $18:120 =$

29) $8:24 =$     36) $8:36 =$     43) $44:82 =$

30) $9:42 =$     37) $16:128 =$     44) $60:240 =$

31) $12:48 =$     38) $14:77 =$     45) $36:180 =$

# *Proportional Ratios*

✍ **Fill in the blanks; solve each proportion.**

1) $3 : 7 \quad = \quad$ __ $: 49$

2) $1 : 2 \quad = \quad 20 :$ __

3) $1 : 5 \quad = \quad$ __ $: 50$

4) $7 : 9 \quad = \quad 14 :$ __

5) $5 : 3 \quad = \quad 45 :$ __

6) $7 : 3 \quad = \quad$ __ $: 18$

7) $10 : 1 \quad = \quad$ __ $: 10$

8) $1 : 3 \quad = \quad$ __ $: 27$

9) $8 : 1 \quad = \quad$ __ $: 8$

10) $9 : 2 \quad = \quad$ __ $: 14$

11) $3 : 12 \quad = \quad 12 :$ __

12) $6 : 4 \quad = \quad 24 :$ __

✍ **State if each pair of ratios form a proportion.**

13) $\frac{3}{10}$ and $\frac{9}{30}$

14) $\frac{1}{2}$ and $\frac{16}{32}$

15) $\frac{5}{6}$ and $\frac{35}{42}$

16) $\frac{3}{7}$ and $\frac{27}{72}$

17) $\frac{2}{5}$ and $\frac{16}{45}$

18) $\frac{4}{9}$ and $\frac{40}{81}$

19) $\frac{6}{11}$ and $\frac{42}{77}$

20) $\frac{1}{6}$ and $\frac{8}{48}$

21) $\frac{6}{17}$ and $\frac{36}{85}$

22) $\frac{2}{7}$ and $\frac{24}{86}$

23) $\frac{12}{19}$ and $\frac{156}{247}$

24) $\frac{13}{21}$ and $\frac{182}{294}$

✍ **Solve each proportion.**

25) $\frac{2}{5} = \frac{14}{x}, x =$ ____

26) $\frac{1}{6} = \frac{7}{x}, x =$ ____

27) $\frac{3}{5} = \frac{27}{x}, x =$ ____

28) $\frac{1}{5} = \frac{x}{80}, x =$ ____

29) $\frac{3}{7} = \frac{x}{63}, x =$ ____

30) $\frac{1}{4} = \frac{13}{x}, x =$ ____

31) $\frac{7}{9} = \frac{56}{x}, x =$ ____

32) $\frac{6}{11} = \frac{42}{x}, x =$ ____

33) $\frac{4}{7} = \frac{x}{77}, x =$ ____

34) $\frac{5}{13} = \frac{x}{143}, x =$ ____

35) $\frac{7}{19} = \frac{x}{209}, x =$ ____

36) $\frac{3}{13} = \frac{x}{195}, x =$ ____

# *Similarity and Ratios*

✎ *Each pair of figures is similar. Find the missing side.*

1)

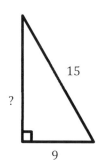

2)

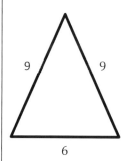 

3)

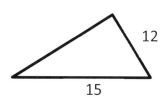 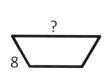

4)

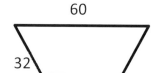

✎ *Solve.*

5) Two rectangles are similar. The first is 6 feet wide and 20 feet long. The second is 15 feet wide. What is the length of the second rectangle? _____

6) Two rectangles are similar. One is 2.5 meters by 9 meters. The longer side of the second rectangle is 22.5 meters. What is the other side of the second rectangle? _____

7) A building casts a shadow 24 ft long. At the same time a girl 5 ft tall casts a shadow 2 ft long. How tall is the building? _____

8) The scale of a map of Texas is 2 inches: 45 miles. If you measure the distance from Dallas to Martin County as 14.4 inches, approximately how far is Martin County from Dallas? _____

# Ratio and Rates Word Problems

✍ *Solve each word problem.*

1) Bob has 12 red cards and 20 green cards. What is the ratio of Bob's red cards to his green cards? _____

2) In a party, 10 soft drinks are required for every 12 guests. If there are 252 guests, how many soft drinks is required? _____

3) In Jack's class, 18 of the students are tall and 10 are short. In Michael's class 54 students are tall and 30 students are short. Which class has a higher ratio of tall to short students? _____

4) The price of 3 apples at the Quick Market is $1.44. The price of 5 of the same apples at Walmart is $2.50. Which place is the better buy? _____

5) The bakers at a Bakery can make 160 bagels in 4 hours. How many bagels can they bake in 16 hours? What is that rate per hour? _____

6) You can buy 5 cans of green beans at a supermarket for $3.40. How much does it cost to buy 35 cans of green beans? _____

7) The ratio of boys to girls in a class is 2:3. If there are 18 boys in the class, how many girls are in that class? _____

8) The ratio of red marbles to blue marbles in a bag is 3:4. If there are 42 marbles in the bag, how many of the marbles are red? _____

# *Percentage Calculations*

 **Calculate the given percent of each value.**

1) 2% of 50 = ____

2) 10% of 30 = ____

3) 20% of 25 = ____

4) 50% of 80 = ____

5) 40% of 200 = ____

6) 20% of 45 = ____

7) 35% of 20 = ____

8) 12% of 400 = ____

9) 40% of 90 = ____

10) 25% of 812 = ____

11) 32% of 600 = ____

12) 87% of 500 = ____

13) 77% of 300 = ____

14) 29% of 86 = ____

15) 33% of 54 = ____

16) 71% of 112 = ____

17) 44% of 165 = ____

18) 17% of 232 = ____

 **Calculate the percent of each given value.**

19) ____% of 7 = 3.5

20) ____% of 15 = 9

21) ____% of 80 = 4

22) ____% of 50 = 12.5

23) ____% of 64 = 8

24) ____% of 72 = 18

25) ____% of 250 = 12.5

26) ____% of 400 = 12

27) ____% of 190 = 9.5

28) ____% of 900 = 126

✍ **Solve each percent problem.**

29) A Cinema has 240 seats. 144 seats were sold for the current movie. What percent of seats are empty? _____ %

30) There are 18 boys and 46 girls in a class. 87.5% of the students in the class take the bus to school. How many students do not take the bus to school? _____

# Percent Problems

✍ **Solve each problem.**

1) 20 is what percent of 50? ____%

2) 18 is what percent of 90? ____%

3) 12 is what percent of 15? ____%

4) 16 is what percent of 200? ____%

5) 24 is what percent of 800? ____%

6) 48 is what percent of 4,00? ____%

7) 90 is what percent of 750? ____%

8) 24 is what percent of 300? ____%

9) 60 is what percent of 400? ____%

10) 42 is what percent of 350? ___%

11) 11 is what percent of 44? ___%

12) 8 is what percent of 64? ___%

13) 210 is what percent of 875? ___%

14) 80 is what percent of 64? ___%

15) 15 is what percent of 12? ___%

16) 56 is what percent of 40? ___%

17) 36 is what percent of 240? ___%

18) 32 is what percent of 20? ___%

✍ **Solve each percent word problem.**

19) There are 18 employees in a company. On a certain day, 36 were present. What percent showed up for work? _____%

20) A metal bar weighs 24 ounces. 15% of the bar is gold. How many ounces of gold are in the bar? _____

21) A crew is made up of 12 women; the rest are men. If 20% of the crew are women, how many people are in the crew? _____

22) There are 48 students in a class and 6 of them are girls. What percent are boys? _____%

23) The Royals softball team played 75 games and won 60 of them. What percent of the games did they lose? _____%

# *Discount, Tax and Tip*

## ✎ *Find the selling price of each item.*

1) Original price of a computer: $500

   Tax: 6%      Selling price: $_____

2) Original price of a laptop: $350

   Tax: 8%      Selling price: $_____

3) Original price of a sofa: $800

   Tax: 7%      Selling price: $_____

4) Original price of a car: $18,500

   Tax: 8.5%    Selling price: $_____

5) Original price of a Table: $250

   Tax: 5%      Selling price: $_____

6) Original price of a house: $250,000

   Tax: 6.5%    Selling price: $_____

7) Original price of a tablet: $400

   Discount: 20%      Selling price: $_____

8) Original price of a chair: $150

   Discount: 15%      Selling price: $_____

9) Original price of a book: $50

   Discount: 25%      Selling price: $_____

10) Original price of a cellphone: $500

   Discount: 10%      Selling price: $_____

11) Food bill: $24

   Tip: 20%            Price: $_____

12) Food bill: $60

   Tipp: 15%           Price: $_____

13) Food bill: $32

   Tip: 20%            Price: $_____

14) Food bill: $18

   Tipp: 25%           Price: $_____

## ✎ *Solve each word problem.*

15) Nicolas hired a moving company. The company charPSAT $400 for its services, and Nicolas gives the movers a 15% tip. How much does Nicolas tip the movers? $_____

16) Mason has lunch at a restaurant and the cost of his meal is $30. Mason wants to leave a 20% tip. What is Mason's total bill including tip? $_____

17) The sales tax in Texas is 8.25% and an item costs $400. How much is the tax? $_____

18) The price of a table at Best Buy is $220. If the sales tax is 6%, what is the final price of the table including tax? $_____

# *Percent of Change*

## ✎ *Find each percent of change.*

1) From 200 to 500.     ___ %

2) From 50 ft to 75 ft.     ___ %

3) From $250 to $350.     ___ %

4) From 60 cm to 90 cm. ___ %

5) From 30 to 90.     ___ %

6) From 30 to 6.     ___ %

7) From 80 to 120.     ___ %

8) From 800 to 200.     ___ %

9) From 25 to 15.     ___ %

10) From 32 to 8.     ___ %

## ✎ *Solve each percent of change word problem.*

11) Bob got a raise, and his hourly wage increased from $12 to $15. What is the percent increase? _____ %

12) The price of a pair of shoes increases from $20 to $32. What is the percent increase? ___ %

13) At a coffeeshop, the price of a cup of coffee increased from $1.20 to $1.44. What is the percent increase in the cost of the coffee? _____ %

14) 6 cm are cut from a 24 cm board. What is the percent decrease in length? _____ %

15) In a class, the number of students has been increased from 18 to 27. What is the percent increase? _____ %

16) The price of gasoline rose from $2.40 to $2.76 in one month. By what percent did the gas price rise? _____ %

17) A shirt was originally priced at $48. It went on sale for $38.40. What was the percent that the shirt was discounted? _____ %

# *Simple Interest*

✍ ***Determine the simple interest for these loans.***

1) $450 at 7% for 2 years. $ _____

2) $5,200 at 4% for 3 years. $ _____

3) $1,300 at 5% for 6 years. $ _____

4) $5,400 at 3.5% for 6 months. $ _____

5) $600 at 4% for 9 months. $ _____

6) $24,000 at 5.5% for 5 years. $ _____

7) $15,600 at 3% for 2 years. $ _____

8) $1,200 at 5.5% for 4 years. $ _____

9) $1,600 at 4.5 % for 9 months. $ _____

10) $12,000 at 2.2% for 5 years. $ _____

✍ ***Solve each simple interest word problem.***

11)    A new car, valued at $28,000, depreciates at 9% per year. What is the value of the car one year after purchase? $_____

12)    Sara puts $4,000 into an investment yielding 5% annual simple interest; she left the money in for five years. How much interest does Sara get at the end of those five years? $_____

13)    A bank is offering 3.5% simple interest on a savings account. If you deposit $7,500, how much interest will you earn in two years? $_____

14)    $400 interest is earned on a principal of $2,000 at a simple interest rate of 5% interest per year. For how many years was the principal invested? _____

15)    In how many years will $1,200 yield an interest of $180 at 3% simple interest? _____

16)    Jim invested $4,000 in a bond at a yearly rate of 4.5%. He earned $540 in interest. How long was the money invested? _____

# *Answers of Worksheets – Chapter 3*

## *Simplifying Ratios*

1) 3 : 2
2) 1 : 10
3) 1 : 12
4) 1 : 2
5) 3 : 50
6) 1 : 6
7) 3 : 7
8) 1 : 2
9) 1 : 5
10) 7 : 9
11) 5 : 3
12) 7 : 3
13) 10 : 1
14) 7 : 9
15) 2 : 5
16) 5 : 7
17) 7 : 9
18) 26 : 41

19) 1 : 3
20) 8 : 1
21) 1 : 2
22) 2 : 9
23) 17 : 20
24) 1 : 10
25) $\frac{1}{2}$
26) $\frac{3}{10}$
27) $\frac{1}{7}$
28) $\frac{2}{11}$
29) $\frac{1}{3}$
30) $\frac{3}{14}$
31) $\frac{1}{4}$
32) $\frac{3}{20}$

33) $\frac{5}{12}$
34) $\frac{9}{41}$
35) $\frac{11}{13}$
36) $\frac{2}{9}$
37) $\frac{1}{8}$
38) $\frac{2}{11}$
39) $\frac{1}{15}$
40) $\frac{1}{3}$
41) $\frac{4}{7}$
42) $\frac{3}{20}$
43) $\frac{22}{41}$
44) $\frac{1}{4}$
45) $\frac{1}{5}$

## *Proportional Ratios*

1) 21
2) 40
3) 10
4) 18
5) 27
6) 42
7) 100
8) 9
9) 64
10) 63
11) 48
12) 16

13) Yes
14) Yes
15) Yes
16) No
17) No
18) No
19) Yes
20) Yes
21) No
22) No
23) Yes
24) Yes

25) 35
26) 42
27) 45
28) 16
29) 27
30) 52
31) 72
32) 77
33) 44
34) 55
35) 77
36) 45

## Similarity and ratios

1) 12
2) 2
3) 5
4) 15
5) 50 feet
6) 6.25 meters
7) 60 feet
8) 324 miles

## Ratio and Rates Word Problems

1) 3 : 5
2) 210
3) The ratio for both classes is 9 to 5.
4) Quick Market is a better buy.
5) 640, the rate is 40 per hour.
6) $23.80
7) 27
8) 18

## Percentage Calculations

1) 1
2) 3
3) 5
4) 40
5) 80
6) 9
7) 7
8) 48
9) 36
10) 203
11) 192
12) 435
13) 231
14) 24.94
15) 17.82
16) 79.52
17) 72.6
18) 39.44
19) 50%
20) 60%
21) 5%
22) 25%
23) 12.5%
24) 25%
25) 5%
26) 3%
27) 5%
28) 14%
29) 40%
30) 8

## Percent Problems

1) 40%
2) 20%
3) 80%
4) 8%
5) 3%
6) 12%
7) 12%
8) 8%
9) 15%
10) 12%
11) 25%
12) 12.5%
13) 24%
14) 125%
15) 125%
16) 140%
17) 15%
18) 160%
19) 75%
20) 3.6 ounces
21) 60
22) 87.5%
23) 20%

## Discount, Tax and Tip

1) $530.00
2) $378.00
3) $856.00
4) $20,072.50
5) $262.50
6) $266,250
7) $320.00
8) $127.50
9) $37.50

10) $450.00
11) $28.80
12) $69.00

13) $38.40
14) $22.50
15) $60.00

16) $36.00
17) $33.00
18) $233.20

## *Percent of Change*

1)  150%
2)  50%
3)  40%
4)  50%
5)  200%
6)  80%

7)  50%
8)  75%
9)  40%
10) 75%
11) 25%
12) 60%

13) 20%
14) 25%
15) 50%
16) 15%
17) 20%

## *Simple Interest*

1)  $63.00
2)  $624.00
3)  $390.00
4)  $94.50
5)  $18.00
6)  $6,600.00

7)  $936.00
8)  $264.00
9)  $54
10) $1,320.00
11) $25,480.00
12) $1,000.00

13)    $525.00
14)    4 years
15)    5 years
16)    3 years

# Chapter 4:

# Algebraic Expressions

## Topics that you'll practice in this chapter:

- ✓ Simplifying Variable Expressions
- ✓ Simplifying Polynomial Expressions
- ✓ Translate Phrases into an Algebraic Statement
- ✓ The Distributive Property
- ✓ Evaluating One Variable Expressions
- ✓ Evaluating Two Variables Expressions
- ✓ Combining like Terms

*Mathematics is, as it were, a sensuous logic, and relates to philosophy as do the arts, music, and plastic art to poetry. — K. Shegel*

# Simplifying Variable Expressions

✎ *Simplify each expression.*

1) $3(x + 9) =$

2) $(-6)(8x - 4) =$

3) $7x + 3 - 3x =$

4) $-2 - x^2 - 6x^2 =$

5) $3 + 10x^2 + 2 =$

6) $8x^2 + 6x + 7x^2 =$

7) $5x^2 - 12x^2 + 8x =$

8) $2x^2 - 2x - x =$

9) $4x + 6(2 - 5x) =$

10) $10x + 8(10x - 6) =$

11) $9(-2x - 6) - 5 =$

12) $2x^2 + (-8x) =$

13) $x - 3 + 5 - 3x =$

14) $2 - 3x + 12 - 2x =$

15) $32x - 4 + 23 + 2x =$

16) $(-6)(8x - 4) + 10x =$

17) $14x - 5(5 - 8x) =$

18) $23x + 4(9x + 3) + 12 =$

19) $3(-7x + 5) + 20x =$

20) $12x - 3x(x + 9) =$

21) $7x + 5x(3 - 3x) =$

22) $5x(-8x + 12) + 14x =$

23) $40x + 12 + 2x^2 =$

24) $5x(x - 3) - 10 =$

25) $8x - 7 + 8x + 2x^2 =$

26) $2x^2 - 5x - 7x =$

27) $7x - 3x^2 - 5x^2 - 3 =$

28) $4 + x^2 - 6x^2 - 12x =$

29) $12x + 8x^2 + 2x + 20 =$

30) $2x^2 + 6x + 3x^2 =$

31) $23 + 15x^2 + 8x - 4x^2 =$

32) $8x - 12x - x^2 + 13 =$

# Simplifying Polynomial Expressions

✍ *Simplify each polynomial.*

1) $(2x^3 + 5x^2) - (12x + 2x^2) =$ _____

2) $(2x^5 + 2x^3) - (7x^3 + 6x^2) =$ _____

3) $(12x^4 + 4x^2) - (2x^2 - 6x^4) =$ _____

4) $14x - 3x^2 - 2(6x^2 + 6x^3) =$ _____

5) $(5x^3 - 3) + 5(2x^2 - 3x^3) =$ _____

6) $(4x^3 - 2x) - 2(4x^3 - 2x^4) =$ _____

7) $2(4x - 3x^3) - 3(3x^3 + 4x^2) =$ _____

8) $(2x^2 - 2x) - (2x^3 + 5x^2) =$ _____

9) $2x^3 - (4x^4 + 2x) + x^2 =$ _____

10) $x^4 - 2(x^2 + x) + 3x =$ _____

11) $(2x^2 - x^4) - (4x^4 - x^2) =$ _____

12) $4x^2 - 5x^3 + 15x^4 - 12x^3 =$ _____

13) $2x^2 - 5x^4 + 14x^4 - 11x^3 =$ _____

14) $2x^2 + 5x^3 - 7x^2 + 12x =$ _____

15) $2x^4 - 5x^5 + 8x^4 - 8x^2 =$ _____

16) $5x^3 + 15x - x^2 - 2x^3 =$ _____

# Translate Phrases into an Algebraic Statement

✍ *Write an algebraic expression for each phrase.*

1) 4 multiplied by $x$. _____

2) Subtract 8 from $y$. _____

3) 6 divided by $x$. _____

4) 12 decreased by $y$. _____

5) Add $y$ to 9. _____

6) The square of 5. _____

7) $x$ raised to the fourth power. _____

8) The sum of nine and a number. _____

9) The difference between sixty–four and $y$. _____

10) The quotient of twelve and a number. _____

11) The quotient of the square of $x$ and 7. _____

12) The difference between $x$ and 8 is 22. _____

13) 2 times $a$ reduced by the square of $b$. _____

14) Subtract the product of $a$ and $b$ from 12. _____

# *The Distributive Property*

✎ *Use the distributive property to simply each expression.*

1) $2(2 + 3x) =$

2) $3(5 + 5x) =$

3) $4(3x - 8) =$

4) $(6x - 2)(-2) =$

5) $(-3)(x + 2) =$

6) $(2 + 2x)5 =$

7) $(-4)(4 - 2x) =$

8) $-(-2 - 5x) =$

9) $(-6x + 2)(-1) =$

10) $(-5)(x - 2) =$

11) $-(7 - 3x) =$

12) $8(8 + 2x) =$

13) $2(12 + 2x) =$

14) $(-6x + 8)4 =$

15) $(3 - 6x)(-7) =$

16) $(-12)(2x + 1) =$

17) $(8 - 2x)9 =$

18) $5(7 + 9x) =$

19) $11(5x + 2) =$

20) $(-4x + 6)6 =$

21) $(3 - 6x)(-8) =$

22) $(-12)(2x - 3) =$

23) $(10 - 2x)9 =$

24) $(-5)(11x - 2) =$

25) $(1 - 9x)(-10) =$

26) $(-6)(x + 8) =$

27) $(-4 + 3x)(-8) =$

28) $(-5)(1 - 11x) =$

29) $11(3x - 12) =$

30) $(-12x + 14)(-5) =$

31) $(-5)(4x - 1) + 4(x + 2) =$

32) $(-3)(x + 4) - (2 + 3x) =$

# *Evaluating One Variable Expressions*

✎ *Evaluate each expression using the value given.*

1) $5 + x$ , $x = 2$

2) $x - 2$, $x = 4$

3) $8x + 1$, $x = 9$

4) $x - 12$, $x = -1$

5) $9 - x$ , $x = 3$

6) $x + 2$, $x = 5$

7) $3x + 7$, $x = 6$

8) $x + (-5)$, $x = -2$

9) $3x + 6$, $x = 4$

10) $4x + 6$, $x = -1$

11) $10 + 2x - 6$, $x = 3$

12) $10 - 3x$, $x = 8$

13) $2x - 5$, $x = 4$

14) $5x + 6$, $x = -3$

15) $12x + 6$, $x = 2$

16) $10 - 3x$, $x = -2$

17) $5(6x + 2)$, $x = 8$

18) $2(-7x - 2)$, $x = 3$

19) $9x - 3x + 12$, $x = 6$

20) $(6x + 3) \div 5$, $x = 2$

21) $(x + 16) \div 3$, $x = 8$

22) $4x - 12 + 8x$, $x = -6$

23) $(16 - 12x)(-2)$, $x = -3$

24) $12x^2 + 5x - 3$, $x = 2$

25) $x^2 - 11x$, $x = -4$

26) $2x(6 - 4x)$, $x = 5$

27) $14x + 7 - 3x^2$, $x = -3$

28) $(-5)(10x - 20 + 2x)$, $x = 2$

29) $(-3) + \frac{x}{4} + 2x$, $x = 16$

30) $(-2) + \frac{x}{7}$, $x = 21$

31) $\left(-\frac{14}{x}\right) - 9 + 4x$, $x = 2$

32) $\left(-\frac{6}{x}\right) - 9 + 2x$, $x = 3$

# *Evaluating Two Variables Expressions*

 **Evaluate each expression using the values given.**

1) $2x + 4y$,

   $x = 3, y = 2$

2) $8x + 5y$,

   $x = 1, y = 5$

3) $-2a + 4b$,

   $a = 6, b = 3$

4) $4x + 7 - 2y$,

   $x = 7, y = 6$

5) $5z + 12 - 4k$,

   $z = 5, k = 2$

6) $2(-x - 2y)$,

   $x = 6, y = 9$

7) $18a + 2b$,

   $a = 2, b = 8$

8) $4x \div 3y$,

   $x = 3, y = 2$

9) $2x + 15 + 4y$,

   $x = -2, y = 4$

10) $4a - (15 - b)$,

   $a = 4, b = 6$

11) $5z + 19 + 8k$,

   $z = -5, k = 4$

12) $xy + 12 + 5x$,

   $x = 7, y = 2$

13) $2x + 4y - 3 + 2$,

   $x = 5, y = 3$

14) $\left(-\frac{12}{x}\right) + 1 + 5y$,

   $x = 6, y = 8$

15) $(-4)(-2a - 2b)$,

   $a = 5, b = 3$

16) $10 + 3x + 7 - 2y$,

   $x = 7, y = 6$

17) $9x + 2 - 4y + 5$,

   $x = 7, y = 5$

18) $6 + 3(-2x - 3y)$,

   $x = 9, y = 7$

19) $2x + 14 + 4y$,

   $x = 6, y = 8$

20) $4a - (5a - b) + 5$,

   $a = 4, b = 6$

# Combining like Terms

✎ *Simplify each expression.*

1) $2x + x + 2 =$

2) $2(5x - 3) =$

3) $7x - 2x + 8 =$

4) $(-4)(3x - 5) =$

5) $9x - 7x - 5 =$

6) $16x - 5 + 8x =$

7) $5 - (5x + 6) =$

8) $-12x + 7 - 10x =$

9) $7x - 11 - 2x + 2 =$

10) $12x + 4x - 21 =$

11) $5 + 2x - 8 =$

12) $(-2x + 6)2 =$

13) $7 + 3x + 6x - 4 =$

14) $9(x - 7x) - 5 =$

15) $7(3x + 6) + 2x =$

16) $3x - 12 - 5x =$

17) $2(4 + 3x) - 7x =$

18) $22x + 6 + 2x =$

19) $(-5x) + 12 + 7x =$

20) $(-3x) - 9 + 15x =$

21) $2(5x + 7) + 8x =$

22) $2(9 - 3x) - 17x =$

23) $-4x - (6 - 14x) =$

24) $(-4) - (3)(5x + 8) =$

25) $(-2)(9x - 3) - 12x =$

26) $-22x + 6 + 4x - 3x =$

27) $4(-13x + 2) - 14x =$

28) $-6x - 19 + 15x =$

29) $21x - 12x + 6 - 7x =$

30) $5(6x + 2x) - 15 =$

31) $18 - 12x - 25 - 15x =$

32) $-3(-4x - 2x) + 8x =$

# *Answers of Worksheets – Chapter 4*

## *Simplifying Variable Expressions*

1)  $3x + 27$
2)  $-48x + 24$
3)  $4x + 3$
4)  $-7x^2 - 2$
5)  $10x^2 + 5$
6)  $15x^2 + 6x$
7)  $-7x^2 + 8x$
8)  $2x^2 - 3x$
9)  $-24x + 12$
10) $90x - 48$

11) $-18x - 59$
12) $2x^2 - 8x$
13) $-2x + 2$
14) $-5x + 14$
15) $34x + 19$
16) $-38x + 24$
17) $54x - 25$
18) $59x + 24$
19) $-x + 15$
20) $-3x^2 - 15x$
21) $-15x^2 + 22x$

22) $-40x^2 + 74x$
23) $2x^2 + 40x + 12$
24) $5x^2 - 15x - 10$
25) $2x^2 + 16x - 7$
26) $2x^2 - 12x$
27) $-8x^2 + 7x - 3$
28) $-5x^2 - 12x + 4$
29) $8x^2 + 14x + 20$
30) $5x^2 + 6x$
31) $11x^2 + 8x + 23$
32) $-x^2 - 4x + 13$

## *Simplifying Polynomial Expressions*

1)  $2x^3 + 3x^2 - 12x$
2)  $2x^5 - 5x^3 - 6x^2$
3)  $18x^4 + 2x^2$
4)  $-12x^3 - 15x^2 + 14x$
5)  $-10x^3 + 10x^2 - 3$
6)  $4x^4 - 4x^3 - 2x$
7)  $-15x^3 - 12x^2 + 8x$
8)  $-2x^3 - 3x^2 - 2x$

9)  $-4x^4 + 2x^3 + x^2 - 2x$
10) $x^4 - 2x^2 + x$
11) $-5x^4 + 3x^2$
12) $15x^4 - 17x^3 + 4x^2$
13) $9x^4 - 11x^3 + 2x^2$
14) $5x^3 - 5x^2 + 12x$
15) $-5x^5 + 10x^4 - 8x^2$
16) $3x^3 - x^2 + 15x$

## *Translate Phrases into an Algebraic Statement*

1)  $4x$
2)  $y - 8$
3)  $\frac{6}{x}$
4)  $12 - y$
5)  $y + 9$

6)  $5^2$
7)  $x^4$
8)  $9 + x$
9)  $64 - y$
10) $\frac{12}{x}$

11) $\frac{x^2}{7}$
12) $x - 8 = 22$
13) $2a - b^2$
14) $12 - ab$

## *The Distributive Property*

1)  $6x + 4$
2)  $15x + 15$
3)  $12x - 32$
4)  $-12x + 4$
5)  $-3x - 6$
6)  $10x + 10$
7)  $8x - 16$
8)  $5x + 2$

9)  $6x - 2$
10) $-5x + 10$
11) $3x - 7$
12) $16x + 64$
13) $4x + 24$
14) $-24x + 32$
15) $42x - 21$
16) $-24x - 12$

17) $-18x + 72$
18) $45x + 35$
19) $55x + 22$
20) $-24x + 36$
21) $48x - 24$
22) $-24x + 36$
23) $-18x + 90$
24) $-55x + 10$

25) $90x - 10$

26) $-6x - 48$

27) $-24x + 32$

28) $55x - 5$

29) $33x - 132$

30) $60x - 70$

31) $-16x + 13$

32) $-6x - 14$

## Evaluating One Variables

1) 7
2) 2
3) 73
4) $-13$
5) 6
6) 7
7) 25
8) $-7$
9) 18
10) 2
11) 10

12) $-14$
13) 3
14) $-9$
15) 30
16) 16
17) 250
18) $-46$
19) 48
20) 3
21) 8
22) $-84$

23) $-104$
24) 55
25) 60
26) $-140$
27) $-62$
28) $-20$
29) 33
30) 1
31) $-8$
32) $-5$

## Evaluating Two Variables

1) 14
2) 33
3) 0
4) 23
5) 29
6) $-48$
7) 52
8) 2

9) 27
10) 7
11) 26
12) 61
13) 21
14) 39
15) 64

16) 26
17) 50
18) $-111$
19) 58
20) 7

## Combining like Terms

1) $3x + 2$
2) $10x - 6$
3) $5x + 8$
4) $-12x + 20$
5) $2x - 5$
6) $24x - 5$
7) $-5x - 1$
8) $-22x + 7$
9) $5x - 9$
10) $16x - 21$
11) $2x - 3$

12) $-4x + 12$
13) $9x + 3$
14) $-54x - 5$
15) $23x + 42$
16) $-2x - 12$
17) $-x + 8$
18) $24x + 6$
19) $2x + 12$
20) $12x - 9$
21) $18x + 14$

22) $-23x + 18$
23) $10x - 6$
24) $-15x - 28$
25) $-30x + 6$
26) $-21x + 6$
27) $-66x + 8$
28) $9x - 19$
29) $2x + 6$
30) $40x - 15$
31) $-27x - 7$
32) $26x$

# Chapter 5:

# Equations and Inequalities

## Topics that you'll practice in this chapter:

✓ One–Step Equations

✓ Multi–Step Equations

✓ Graphing Single–Variable Inequalities

✓ One–Step Inequalities

✓ Multi-Step Inequalities

✓ Systems of Equations

✓ Systems of Equations Word Problems

✓ Quadratic Equations

*"Life is a math equation. In order to gain the most, you have to know how to convert negatives into positives." – Anonymous*

# One–Step Equations

✎ *Solve each equation.*

1) $2x = 20, x = $ ____

2) $4x = 16, x = $ ____

3) $8x = 24, x = $ ____

4) $6x = 30, x = $ ____

5) $x + 5 = 8, x = $ ____

6) $x - 1 = 5, x = $ ____

7) $x - 8 = 3, x = $ ____

8) $x + 6 = 12, x = $ ____

9) $x - 2 = 17, x = $ ____

10) $8 = 12 + x, x = $ ____

11) $x - 5 = 4, x = $ ____

12) $2 - x = -12, x = $ ____

13) $16 = -4 + x, x = $ ____

14) $x - 4 = -25, x = $ ____

15) $x + 12 = -9, x = $ ____

16) $14 = 18 - x, x = $ ____

17) $2 + x = -14, x = $ ____

18) $x - 5 = 15, x = $ ____

19) $25 = x - 5, x = $ ____

20) $x - 3 = -12, x = $ ____

21) $x - 12 = 12, x = $ ____

22) $x - 12 = -25, x = $ ____

23) $x - 13 = 32, x = $ ____

24) $-55 = x - 18, x = $ ____

25) $x - 12 = 18, x = $ ____

26) $20 = 5x, x = $ ____

27) $x - 30 = 20, x = $ ____

28) $x - 12 = 32, x = $ ____

29) $36 - x = 3, x = $ ____

30) $x - 14 = 14, x = $ ____

31) $19 - x = -15, x = $ ____

32) $x - 19 = -35, x = $ ____

# Multi–Step Equations

✏️ *Solve each equation.*

1) $2x + 3 = 5$

2) $-x + 8 = 5$

3) $3x - 4 = 5$

4) $-(2 - x) = 5$

5) $2x - 18 = 12$

6) $4x - 2 = 6$

7) $2x - 14 = 4$

8) $5x + 10 = 25$

9) $8x + 9 = 25$

10) $-3(2 + x) = 3$

11) $-2(4 + x) = 4$

12) $20 = -(x - 8)$

13) $2(2 - 2x) = 20$

14) $-12 = -(2x + 8)$

15) $5(2 + x) = 5$

16) $2(x - 14) = 4$

17) $-28 = 2x + 12x$

18) $3x + 15 = -x - 5$

19) $2(3 + 2x) = -18$

20) $12 - 2x = -8 - x$

21) $10 - 3x = 14 + x$

22) $10 + 10x = -2 + 4x$

23) $24 = (-4x) - 8 + 8$

24) $12 = 2x - 12 + 6x$

25) $-12 = -4x - 6 + 2x$

26) $4x - 12 = -18 + 5x$

27) $5x - 10 = 2x + 5$

28) $-7 - 3x = 2(3 - 2x)$

29) $x - 2 = -3(6 - 3x)$

30) $10x - 56 = 12x - 114$

31) $4x - 8 = -4(11 + 2x)$

32) $-5x - 14 = 6x + 52$

# *Graphing Single–Variable Inequalities*

✍ *Draw a graph for each inequality.*

1) $x > 2$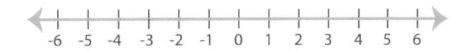

2) $x < 5$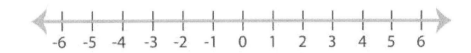

3) $x > -1$

4) $x > 3$

5) $x < -5$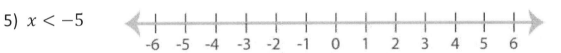

6) $x > -2$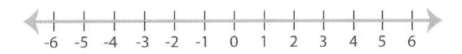

7) $x < 0$

8) $x > 4$

# One–Step Inequalities

 *Solve each inequality and graph it.*

1) $x + 2 \geq 3$

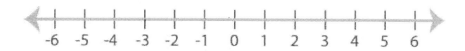

2) $x - 1 \leq 2$

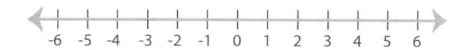

3) $2x \geq 12$

4) $4 + x \leq 5$

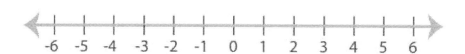

5) $x + 3 \leq -3$

6) $4x \geq 16$

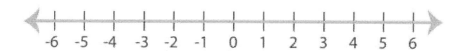

7) $9x \leq 18$

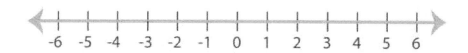

8) $x + 2 \geq 7$

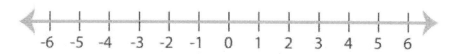

# Multi-Step Inequalities

✎ *Solve each inequality.*

1) $x - 2 \le 6$

2) $3 - x \le 3$

3) $2x - 4 \le 8$

4) $3x - 5 \ge 16$

5) $x - 5 \ge 10$

6) $2x - 8 \le 6$

7) $8x - 2 \le 14$

8) $-5 + 3x \le 10$

9) $2(x - 3) \le 6$

10) $7x - 5 \le 9$

11) $4x - 21 < 19$

12) $2x - 3 < 21$

13) $17 - 3x \ge -13$

14) $9 + 4x < 21$

15) $3 + 2x \ge 19$

16) $6 + 2x < 32$

17) $4x - 1 < 7$

18) $3(3 - 2x) \ge -15$

19) $-(3 + 4x) < 13$

20) $20 - 8x \ge -28$

21) $-3(x - 7) > 21$

22) $\dfrac{2x + 6}{4} \le 10$

23) $\dfrac{4x + 8}{2} \le 12$

24) $\dfrac{3x - 8}{7} > 1$

25) $4 + \dfrac{x}{3} < 7$

26) $\dfrac{9x}{7} - 7 < 2$

27) $\dfrac{4x + 12}{4} > 1$

28) $15 + \dfrac{x}{5} < 12$

# Systems of Equations

 **Solve each system of equations.**

1) $-2x + 2y = 4$     $x = $ ___

    $-2x + y = 3$     $y = $ ___

2) $-10x + 2y = -6$     $x = $ ___

    $6x - 16y = 48$     $y = $ ___

3) $y = -8$     $x = $ ___

    $16x - 12y = 32$

4) $2y = -6x + 10$     $x = $ ___

    $10x - 8y = -6$     $y = $ ___

5) $10x - 9y = -13$     $x = $ ___

    $-5x + 3y = 11$     $y = $ ___

6) $-3x - 4y = 5$     $x = $ ___

    $x - 2y = 5$     $y = $ ___

7) $5x - 14y = -23$     $x = $ ___

    $-6x + 7y = 8$     $y = $ ___

8) $10x - 14y = -4$     $x = $ ___

    $-10x - 20y = -30$     $y = $ ___

9) $-4x + 12y = 12$     $x = $ ___

    $-14x + 16y = -10$     $y = $ ___

10) $x + 20y = 56$     $x = $ ___

    $x + 15y = 41$     $y = $ ___

11) $6x - 7y = -8$     $x = $ ___

    $-x - 4y = -9$     $y = $ ___

12) $-3x + 2y = -18$     $x = $ ___

    $8x - 2y = 28$     $y = $ ___

13) $-5x + y = -3$     $x = $ ___

    $3x - 8y = 24$     $y = $ ___

14) $3x - 2y = 2$     $x = $ ___

    $5x - 5y = 10$     $y = $ ___

15) $8x + 14y = 4$     $x = $ ___

    $-6x - 7y = -10$     $y = $ ___

16) $10x + 7y = 1$     $x = $ ___

    $-5x - 7y = 24$     $y = $ ___

# *Systems of Equations Word Problems*

✍ *Solve each word problem.*

1) Tickets to a movie cost $5 for adults and $3 for students. A group of friends purchased 18 tickets for $82.00. How many adults ticket did they buy? _____

2) At a store, Eva bought two shirts and five hats for $154.00. Nicole bought three same shirts and four same hats for $168.00. What is the price of each shirt? _____

3) A farmhouse shelters 10 animals, some are pigs, and some are ducks. Altogether there are 36 legs. How many pigs are there? _____

4) A class of 195 students went on a field trip. They took 19 vehicles, some cars and some buses. If each car holds 5 students and each bus hold 25 students, how many buses did they take? _____

5) A theater is selling tickets for a performance. Mr. Smith purchased 8 senior tickets and 5 child tickets for $136 for his friends and family. Mr. Jackson purchased 4 senior tickets and 6 child tickets for $96. What is the price of a senior ticket? $_____

6) The difference of two numbers is 6. Their sum is 14. What is the bigger number? $_____

7) The sum of the digits of a certain two-digit number is 7. Reversing its digits increase the number by 9. What is the number? _____

8) The difference of two numbers is 18. Their sum is 66. What are the numbers? _____

9) The length of a rectangle is 3 meters greater than 2 times the width. The perimeter of rectangle is 30 meters. What is the length of the rectangle? _____

10) Jim has 44 nickels and dimes totaling $2.95. How many nickels does he have? _____

# *Quadratic Equation*

## ✎ *Multiply.*

1) $(x - 2)(x + 4) = $ _____

2) $(x + 1)(x + 6) = $ _____

3) $(x - 4)(x + 2) = $ _____

4) $(x + 5)(x - 3) = $ _____

5) $(x - 6)(x - 2) = $ _____

6) $(2x + 1)(x - 3) = $ _____

7) $(2x - 1)(x + 4) = $ _____

8) $(2x - 3)(x + 4) = $ _____

9) $(3x + 5)(x - 3) = $ _____

10) $(3x + 4)(2x - 2) = $ _____

## ✎ *Factor each expression.*

11) $x^2 - 5x + 4 = $ _____

12) $x^2 + 6x + 8 = $ _____

13) $x^2 + x - 12 = $ _____

14) $x^2 - 7x + 10 = $ _____

15) $x^2 - 4x - 12 = $ _____

16) $2x^2 - 3x - 2 = $ _____

17) $2x^2 + 8x + 8 = $ _____

18) $3x^2 - 14x + 5 = $ _____

19) $3x^2 + 4x + 1 = $ _____

20) $4x^2 - 12x + 8 = $ _____

## ✎ *Solve each equation.*

21) $(x + 2)(x - 4) = 0$

22) $(x + 5)(x + 8) = 0$

23) $(2x + 4)(x + 3) = 0$

24) $(3x - 9)(2x + 6) = 0$

25) $x^2 - 11x + 19 = -5$

26) $x^2 + 7x + 18 = 8$

27) $x^2 - 10x + 22 = -2$

28) $x^2 + 3x - 12 = 6$

29) $5x^2 - 5x - 10 = 0$

30) $6x^2 - 6x = 36$

# *Answers of Worksheets – Chapter 5*

## *One–Step Equations*

| | | |
|---|---|---|
| 1) 10 | 12) 14 | 23) 45 |
| 2) 4 | 13) 20 | 24) $-37$ |
| 3) 3 | 14) $-21$ | 25) 30 |
| 4) 5 | 15) $-21$ | 26) 4 |
| 5) 3 | 16) 4 | 27) 50 |
| 6) 6 | 17) $-16$ | 28) 42 |
| 7) 11 | 18) 20 | 29) 33 |
| 8) 6 | 19) 30 | 30) 28 |
| 9) 19 | 20) $-9$ | 31) 34 |
| 10) $-4$ | 21) 24 | 32) $-16$ |
| 11) 9 | 22) $-13$ | |

## *Multi–Step Equations*

| | | |
|---|---|---|
| 1) 1 | 12) $-12$ | 23) $-6$ |
| 2) 3 | 13) $-4$ | 24) 3 |
| 3) 3 | 14) 2 | 25) 3 |
| 4) 7 | 15) $-1$ | 26) 6 |
| 5) 15 | 16) 16 | 27) 5 |
| 6) 2 | 17) $-2$ | 28) 13 |
| 7) 9 | 18) $-5$ | 29) 2 |
| 8) 3 | 19) $-6$ | 30) 29 |
| 9) 2 | 20) 20 | 31) $-3$ |
| 10) $-3$ | 21) $-1$ | 32) $-6$ |
| 11) $-6$ | 22) $-2$ | |

## *Graphing Single–Variable Inequalities*

1)

2)

3)

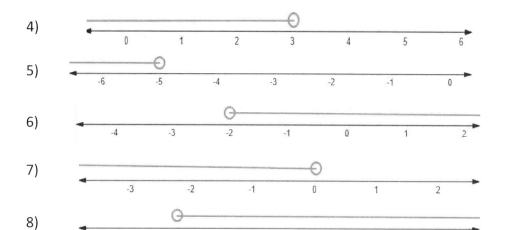

4)

5)

6)

7)

8)

## One–Step Inequalities

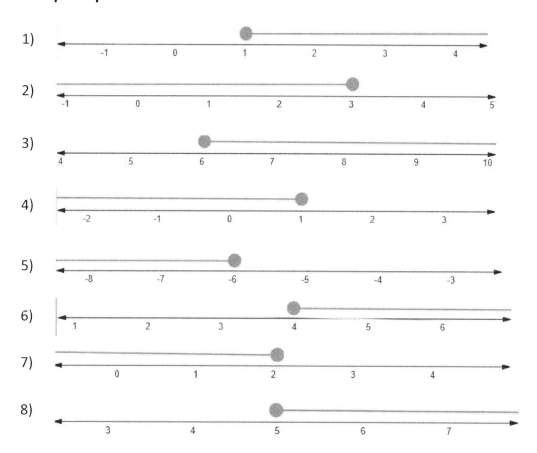

1)

2)

3)

4)

5)

6)

7)

8)

## Multi-Step Inequalities

1) $x \leq 8$     4) $x \geq 7$     7) $x \leq 2$
2) $x \geq 0$     5) $x \geq 15$    8) $x \leq 5$
3) $x \leq 6$     6) $x \leq 7$     9) $x \leq 6$

10) $x \leq 2$

11) $x < 10$

12) $x < 12$

13) $x \leq 10$

14) $x < 3$

15) $x \geq 8$

16) $x < 13$

17) $x < 2$

18) $x \leq 4$

19) $x > -4$

20) $x \leq 6$

21) $x < 0$

22) $x \leq 17$

23) $x \leq 4$

24) $x > 5$

25) $x < 9$

26) $x < 7$

27) $x > -2$

28) $x < -15$

## Systems of Equations

1) $x = -1, y = 1$

2) $x = 0, y = -3$

3) $x = -4$

4) $x = 1, y = 2$

5) $x = -4, y = -3$

6) $x = 1, y = -2$

7) $x = 1, y = 2$

8) $x = 1, y = 1$

9) $x = 3, y = 2$

10) $x = -4, y = 3$

11) $x = 1, y = 2$

12) $x = 2, y = -6$

13) $x = 0, y = -3$

14) $x = -2, y = -4$

15) $x = 4, y = -2$

16) $x = 5, y = -7$

## Systems of Equations Word Problems

1) 14

2) $32

3) 8

4) 5

5) $12

6) 10

7) 34

8) $42, 24$

9) 11 *meters*

10) 29

## Quadratic Equations

1) $x^2 + 2x - 8$

2) $x^2 + 7x + 6$

3) $x^2 - 2x - 8$

4) $x^2 + 2x - 15$

5) $x^2 - 8x + 12$

6) $2x^2 - 5x - 3$

7) $2x^2 + 7x - 4$

8) $2x^2 + 5x - 12$

9) $3x^2 - 4x - 15$

10) $6x^2 + 2x - 8$

11) $(x - 4)(x - 1)$

12) $(x + 4)(x + 2)$

13) $(x - 3)(x + 4)$

14) $(x - 5)(x - 2)$

15) $(x + 2)(x - 6)$

16) $(2x + 1)(x - 2)$

17) $(2x + 4)(x + 2)$

18) $(3x - 1)(x + 5)$

19) $(3x + 1)(x + 1)$

20) $(2x - 2)(2x - 4)$

21) $x = -2, x = 4$

22) $x = -5, x = -8$

23) $x = -2, x = -3$

24) $x = 3, x = -3$

25) $x = 3, x = 8$

26) $x = -2, x = -5$

27) $x = 4, x = 6$

28) $x = 3, x = -6$

29) $x = 2, x = -1$

30) $x = -2, x = 3$

# Chapter 6:

# Linear Functions

**Topics that you'll practice in this chapter:**

- ✓ Finding Slope
- ✓ Graphing Lines Using Line Equation
- ✓ Writing Linear Equations
- ✓ Graphing Linear Inequalities
- ✓ Finding Midpoint
- ✓ Finding Distance of Two Points

*"Nature is written in mathematical language." – Galileo Galilei*

# Finding Slope

✎ **Find the slope of each line.**

1) $y = x - 1$

2) $y = -2x + 5$

3) $y = 2x - 1$

4) $y = -x - 8$

5) $y = 6 + 5x$

6) $y = 2 - 3x$

7) $y = 4x + 12$

8) $y = -6x + 2$

9) $y = -x + 8$

10) $y = 7x - 5$

11) $y = \frac{1}{2}x + 3$

12) $y = -\frac{2}{3}x + 1$

13) $-x + 2y = 5$

14) $2x + 2y = 6$

15) $8y - 2x = 10$

16) $5y - x = 2$

✎ **Find the slope of the line through each pair of points.**

17) $(1, 1), (2, 3)$

18) $(-1, 2), (0, 3)$

19) $(3, -1), (2, 3)$

20) $(-2, -1), (0, 5)$

21) $(5, 1), (2, 4)$

22) $(-3, 1), (-2, 4)$

23) $(6, 2), (7, 4)$

24) $(6, -5), (3, 4)$

25) $(12, -9), (11, -8)$

26) $(7, 4), (5, -2)$

27) $(1, 1), (3, 5)$

28) $(7, -12), (5, 10)$

# *Graphing Lines Using Line Equation*

✎ ***Sketch the graph of each line.***

1) $y = 3x - 2$

2) $y = -x + 1$

3) $x + y = 4$

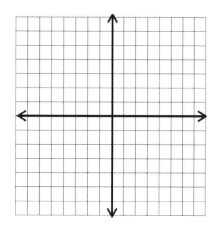
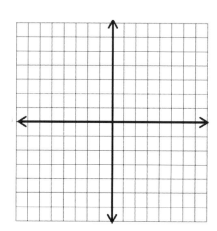
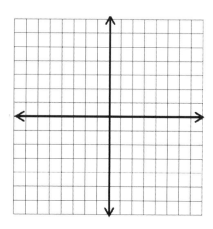

4) $x - y = -5$

5) $2x - y = -4$

6) $3x - 2y = -6$

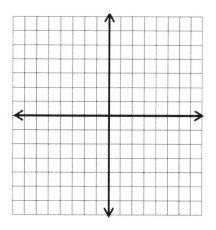
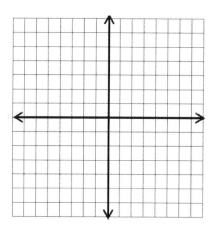
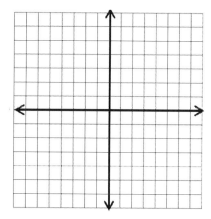

# *Writing Linear Equations*

 **Write the equation of the line through the given points.**

1) through: $(1, -2), (2, 3)$

2) through: $(-2, 1), (1, 4)$

3) through: $(-2, 1), (0, 5)$

4) through: $(5, 4), (2, 1)$

5) through: $(-4, 9), (3, 2)$

6) through: $(8, 3), (7, 2)$

7) through: $(7, -2), (5, 2)$

8) through: $(-3, 9), (5, -7)$

9) through: $(6, 8), (4, 14)$

10) through: $(5, 9), (7, -3)$

11) through: $(-2, 8), (-6, -4)$

12) through: $(3, 3), (1, -5)$

13) through: $(8, -5), (-5, 8)$

14) through: $(2, -6), (-1, 3)$

15) through: $(5, 5), (2, -4)$

16) through: $(-1, 8), (2, -7)$

 **Solve each problem.**

17) What is the equation of a line with slope 2 and intercept 4? _____

18) What is the equation of a line with slope 4 and intercept 12? _____

19) What is the equation of a line with slope 4 and passes through point $(4, 2)$?

_____

20) What is the equation of a line with slope $-2$ and passes through point $(-2, 4)$?

_____

21) The slope of a line is $-3$ and it passes through point $(-1, 5)$. What is the equation of

the line? _____

22) The slope of a line is 3 and it passes through point $(-1, 4)$. What is the equation of the

line? _____

# Graphing Linear Inequalities

✎ *Sketch the graph of each linear inequality.*

1) $y > 3x - 1$

2) $y < -x + 4$

3) $y \leq -5x + 8$

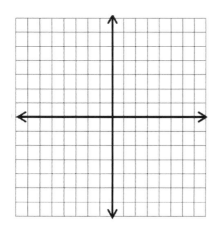 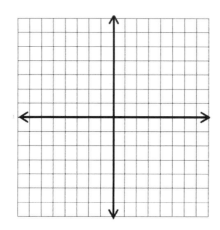 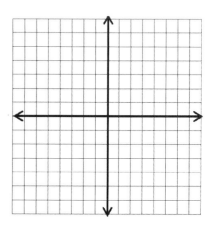

4) $2y \geq 8 + 6x$

5) $y < 2x - 3$

6) $4y \leq -6x + 2$

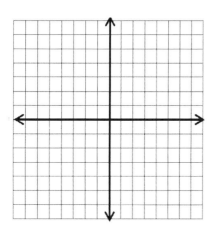 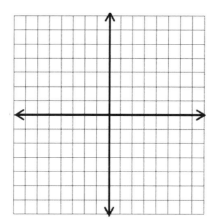 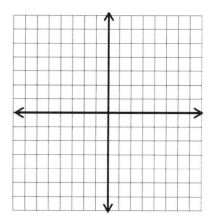

# *Finding Midpoint*

 **Find the midpoint of the line segment with the given endpoints.**

1) $(-2, -2), (0, 2)$

2) $(5, 1), (-2, 4)$

3) $(4, -1), (0, 3)$

4) $(-3, 5), (-1, 3)$

5) $(3, -2), (7, -6)$

6) $(-4, -3), (2, -7)$

7) $(5, 0), (-5, 8)$

8) $(-6, 4), (-2, 0)$

9) $(-3, 4), (9, -6)$

10) $(2, 8), (6, -2)$

11) $(4, 7), (-6, 5)$

12) $(9, 3), (-1, -7)$

13) $(-4, 12), (-2, 6)$

14) $(14, 5), (8, -1)$

15) $(11, 7), (-3, 1)$

16) $(-7, -4), (-3, 8)$

17) $(13, 7), (5, 11)$

18) $(-5, -10), (9, -2)$

19) $(8, 15), (-2, 7)$

20) $(13, -2), (5, 10)$

21) $(2, -2), (3, -5)$

22) $(0, 2), (-2, -6)$

23) $(7, 4), (9, -1)$

24) $(4, -5), (0, 8)$

 **Solve each problem.**

25) One endpoint of a line segment is $(1, 2)$ and the midpoint of the line segment is $(-1, 4)$. What is the other endpoint? _____

26) One endpoint of a line segment is $(-3, 6)$ and the midpoint of the line segment is $(5, 2)$. What is the other endpoint? _____

27) One endpoint of a line segment is $(-2, -6)$ and the midpoint of the line segment is $(6, 8)$. What is the other endpoint? _____

# *Finding Distance of Two Points*

✍ **Find the distance between each pair of points.**

$$\sqrt{(x_2 - x_1)^2 + (y_2 - y_1)^2}$$

1) $(2, 1), (-1, -3)$

2) $(-2, -1), (2, 2)$

3) $(-1, 0), (5, 8)$

4) $(-4, -1), (1, 11)$

5) $(3, -2), (-6, -14)$

6) $(-6, 0), (-2, 3)$

7) $(3, 2), (11, 17)$

8) $(-6, -10), (6, -1)$

9) $(5, 9), (-11, -3)$

10) $(9, -3), (3, -11)$

11) $(2, 0), (12, 24)$

12) $(8, 4), (3, -8)$

13) $(4, 2), (-5, -10)$

14) $(-5, 6), (3, 21)$

15) $(0, 8), (-4, 5)$

16) $(-8, -5), (4, 0)$

17) $(3, 5), (-5, -10)$

18) $(-2, 3), (22, 13)$

19) $(7, 2), (-8, -18)$

20) $(-5, 4), (7, 9)$

✍ **Solve each problem.**

21) Triangle ABC is a right triangle on the coordinate system and its vertices are $(-2, 5)$, $(-2, 1)$, and $(1, 1)$. What is the area of triangle ABC? _____

22) Three vertices of a triangle on a coordinate system are $(1, 1)$, $(1, 4)$, and $(5, 4)$. What is the perimeter of the triangle? _____

23) Four vertices of a rectangle on a coordinate system are $(2, 5)$, $(2, 2)$, $(6, 5)$, and $(6, 2)$. What is its perimeter? _____

# Answers of Worksheets – Chapter 6

## Finding Slope

1) 1
2) $-2$
3) 2
4) $-1$
5) 5
6) $-3$
7) 4
8) $-6$
9) $-1$
10) 7

11) $\frac{1}{2}$
12) $-\frac{2}{3}$
13) $\frac{1}{2}$
14) $-1$
15) $\frac{1}{4}$
16) $\frac{1}{5}$
17) 2
18) 1

19) $-4$
20) 3
21) $-1$
22) 3
23) 2
24) $-3$
25) $-1$
26) 3
27) 2
28) $-11$

## Graphing Lines Using Line Equation

1) $y = 3x - 2$

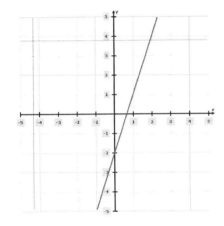

2) $y = -x + 1$

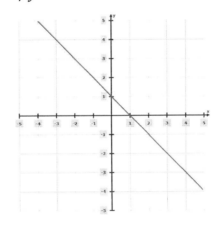

3) $x + y = 4$

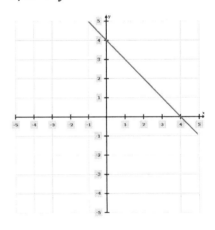

4) $x - y = -5$

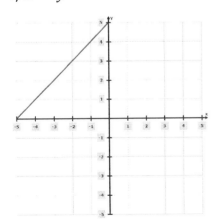

5) $2x - y = -4$

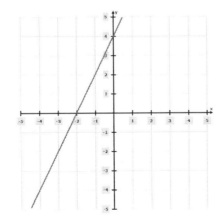

6) $3x - 2y = -6$

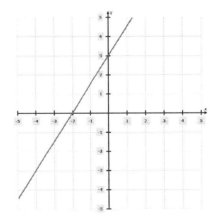

## Writing Linear Equations

1) $y = 5x - 7$
2) $y = x + 3$
3) $y = 2x + 5$
4) $y = x - 1$
5) $y = -x + 5$
6) $y = x - 5$
7) $y = -2x + 12$
8) $y = -2x + 3$

9) $y = -3x + 26$
10) $y = -6x + 39$
11) $y = 3x + 14$
12) $y = 4x - 9$
13) $y = -x + 3$
14) $y = -3x$
15) $y = 3x - 10$
16) $y = -5x + 3$

17) $y = 2x + 4$
18) $y = 4x + 12$
19) $y = 4x - 14$
20) $y = -2x + 8$
21) $y = -3x + 2$
22) $y = 3x + 7$

## Graphing Linear Inequalities

1) $y > 3x - 1$

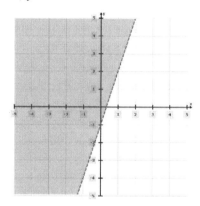

2) $y < -x + 4$

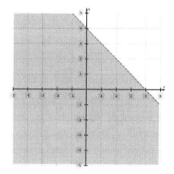

3) $y \leq -5x + 8$

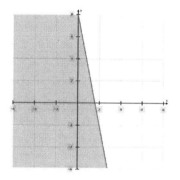

4) $2y \geq 8 + 6x$

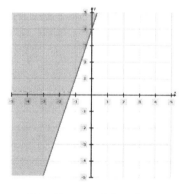

5) $y < 2x - 3$

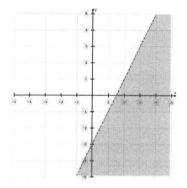

6) $4y \leq -6x + 2$

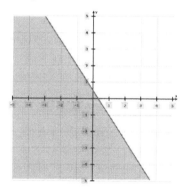

## Finding Midpoint

1) $(-1, 0)$
2) $(1.5, 2.5)$
3) $(2, 1)$
4) $(-2, 4)$
5) $(5, -4)$

6) $(-1, -5)$
7) $(0, 4)$
8) $(-4, 2)$
9) $(3, -1)$
10) $(4, 3)$

11) $(-1, 6)$
12) $(4, -2)$
13) $(-3, 9)$
14) $(11, 2)$
15) $(4, 4)$

16) $(-5, 2)$
17) $(9, 9)$
18) $(2, -6)$
19) $(3, 11)$

20) $(9, 4)$
21) $(2.5, -3.5)$
22) $(-1, -2)$
23) $(8, 1.5)$

24) $(2, 1.5)$
25) $(-3, 6)$
26) $(13, -2)$
27) $(14, 22)$

## Finding Distance of Two Points

1) 5
2) 5
3) 10
4) 13
5) 15
6) 5
7) 17
8) 15

9) 20
10) 10
11) 26
12) 13
13) 15
14) 17
15) 5
16) 13

17) 17
18) 26
19) 25
20) 13
21) 6 *square units*
22) 12 *units*
23) 14 *units*

# Chapter 7:

# Exponents

## Topics that you'll practice in this chapter:

- ✓ Multiplication Property of Exponents
- ✓ Zero and Negative Exponents
- ✓ Division Property of Exponents
- ✓ Powers of Products and Quotients
- ✓ Negative Exponents and Negative Bases
- ✓ Scientific Notation
- ✓ Square Roots

*Mathematics is no more computation than typing is literature.*

*– John Allen Paulos*

# Multiplication Property of Exponents

✎ *Simplify and write the answer in exponential form.*

1) $2 \times 2^2 =$

2) $5^3 \times 5 =$

3) $3^2 \times 3^2 =$

4) $4^2 \times 4^2 =$

5) $7^3 \times 7^2 \times 7 =$

6) $2 \times 2^2 \times 2^2 =$

7) $5^3 \times 5^2 \times 5 \times 5 =$

8) $2x \times x =$

9) $x^3 \times x^2 =$

10) $x^4 \times x^4 =$

11) $x^2 \times x^2 \times x^2 =$

12) $6x \times 6x =$

13) $2x^2 \times 2x^2 =$

14) $3x^2 \times x =$

15) $4x^4 \times 4x^4 \times 4x^4 =$

16) $2x^2 \times x^2 =$

17) $x^4 \times 3x =$

18) $x \times 2x^2 =$

19) $5x^4 \times 5x^4 =$

20) $2yx^2 \times 2x =$

21) $3x^4 \times y^2x^4 =$

22) $y^2x^3 \times y^5x^2 =$

23) $4yx^3 \times 2x^2y^3 =$

24) $6x^2 \times 6x^3y^4 =$

25) $3x^4y^5 \times 7x^2y^3 =$

26) $7x^2y^5 \times 9xy^3 =$

27) $7xy^4 \times 4x^3y^3 =$

28) $3x^5y^3 \times 8x^2y^3 =$

29) $3x \times y^5x^3 \times y^4 =$

30) $yx^2 \times 2y^2x^2 \times 2xy =$

31) $4yx^4 \times 5y^5x \times xy^3 =$

32) $7x^3 \times 10y^3x^5 \times 8yx^3 =$

# Zero and Negative Exponents

✍ *Evaluate the following expressions.*

1) $1^{-1} =$

2) $2^{-2} =$

3) $0^{15} =$

4) $1^{-10} =$

5) $8^{-1} =$

6) $8^{-2} =$

7) $2^{-4} =$

8) $10^{-2} =$

9) $9^{-1} =$

10) $3^{-2} =$

11) $7^{-2} =$

12) $3^{-4} =$

13) $6^{-2} =$

14) $5^{-3} =$

15) $22^{-1=}$

16) $4^{-2} =$

17) $5^{-2} =$

18) $35^{-1} =$

19) $4^{-3} =$

20) $6^{-3} =$

21) $3^{-5} =$

22) $5^{-2} =$

23) $2^{-3} =$

24) $3^{-3} =$

25) $7^{-3} =$

26) $6^{-3} =$

27) $8^{-3} =$

28) $9^{-2} =$

29) $10^{-3} =$

30) $10^{-9} =$

31) $\left(\frac{1}{2}\right)^{-1}$

32) $\left(\frac{1}{2}\right)^{-2} =$

33) $\left(\frac{1}{3}\right)^{-2} =$

34) $\left(\frac{2}{3}\right)^{-2} =$

35) $\left(\frac{1}{5}\right)^{-3} =$

36) $\left(\frac{3}{4}\right)^{-2} =$

37) $\left(\frac{2}{5}\right)^{-2} =$

38) $\left(\frac{1}{2}\right)^{-8} =$

39) $\left(\frac{2}{5}\right)^{-3} =$

40) $\left(\frac{3}{7}\right)^{-2} =$

41) $\left(\frac{5}{6}\right)^{-3} =$

42) $\left(\frac{4}{9}\right)^{-2} =$

# Division Property of Exponents

✎ **Simplify.**

1) $\dfrac{2^2}{2^3} =$

2) $\dfrac{2^4}{2^2} =$

3) $\dfrac{5^5}{5} =$

4) $\dfrac{3}{3^5} =$

5) $\dfrac{x}{x^3} =$

6) $\dfrac{3 \times 3^3}{3^2 \times 3^4} =$

7) $\dfrac{5^8}{5^3} =$

8) $\dfrac{5 \times 5^6}{5^2 \times 5^7} =$

9) $\dfrac{3^4 \times 3^7}{3^2 \times 3^8} =$

10) $\dfrac{5x}{10x^3} =$

11) $\dfrac{3x^3}{2x^5} =$

12) $\dfrac{12x^3}{14^6} =$

13) $\dfrac{12x^3}{9y^8} =$

14) $\dfrac{25xy^4}{5x^6y^2} =$

15) $\dfrac{2x^4}{7x} =$

16) $\dfrac{16 \; ^2 y^8}{4x^3} =$

17) $\dfrac{12 \; ^4}{15 \; ^7 y^9} =$

18) $\dfrac{12yx^4}{10yx^8} =$

19) $\dfrac{16x^4y}{9x^8y^2} =$

20) $\dfrac{5x^8}{20x^8} =$

21) $\dfrac{2x^{-5}}{9x^{-2}} =$

# Powers of Products and Quotients

✎ *Simplify.*

1) $(4^2)^2 =$

2) $(6^2)^3 =$

3) $(2 \times 2^3)^4 =$

4) $(4 \times 4^4)^2 =$

5) $(3^3 \times 3^2)^3 =$

6) $(5^4 \times 5^5)^2 =$

7) $(2 \times 2^4)^2 =$

8) $(2^6)^2 =$

9) $(11x^5)^2 =$

10) $(4x^2y^4)^4 =$

11) $(2x^4y^4)^3 =$

12) $(3x^2y^2)^2 =$

13) $(3x^4y^3)^4 =$

14) $(2x^6y^8)^2 =$

15) $(12x^3x)^3 =$

16) $(2x^9x^6)^3 =$

17) $(5x^{10}y^3)^3 =$

18) $(4x^3x^3)^2 =$

19) $(3x^3.5x)^2 =$

20) $(10x^{11}y^3)^2 =$

21) $(9x^7y^5)^2 =$

22) $(4x^4y^6)^5 =$

23) $(3x.4y^3)^2 =$

24) $(\frac{5x}{x^2})^2 =$

25) $\left(\frac{x^4y^4}{x^2y^2}\right)^3 =$

26) $\left(\frac{25}{5x^6}\right)^2 =$

27) $\left(\frac{x^8}{x^6y^2}\right)^2 =$

28) $\left(\frac{xy^2}{x^3y^3}\right)^{-2} =$

29) $\left(\frac{2xy^4}{x^3}\right)^2 =$

30) $\left(\frac{xy^4}{5xy^2}\right)^{-3} =$

# Negative Exponents and Negative Bases

✎ *Simplify.*

1) $-6^{-1} =$

2) $-5^{-2} =$

3) $-2^{-4} =$

4) $-x^{-3} =$

5) $2x^{-1} =$

6) $-4x^{-3} =$

7) $-12x^{-5} =$

8) $-5x^{-2}y^{-3} =$

9) $20x^{-4}y^{-1} =$

10) $14a^{-6}b^{-7} =$

11) $-12x^2y^{-3} =$

12) $-\dfrac{25}{x^{-6}} =$

13) $-\dfrac{2x}{a^{-4}} =$

14) $\left(-\dfrac{1}{3}\right)^{-2} =$

15) $\left(-\dfrac{3}{4}\right)^{-2} =$

16) $-\dfrac{9}{a^{-7}b^{-2}} =$

17) $-\dfrac{5x}{x^{-3}} =$

18) $-\dfrac{a^{-3}}{b^{-2}} =$

19) $-\dfrac{5}{x^{-3}} =$

20) $\dfrac{7b}{-9c^{-4}} =$

21) $\dfrac{7a}{a^{-3}b^{-1}} =$

22) $-\dfrac{5n^{-2}}{10^{-3}} =$

23) $\dfrac{4ab^{-2}}{-3c^{-2}} =$

24) $\left(\dfrac{3a}{2c}\right)^{-2} =$

25) $\left(-\dfrac{5x}{3yz}\right)^{-3} =$

26) $\dfrac{4a^{-2}}{-3c^{-2}} =$

27) $\left(-\dfrac{x^3}{x^4}\right)^{-2} =$

28) $\left(-\dfrac{x^{-2}}{3x^2}\right)^{-3} =$

29) $\left(-\dfrac{x^{-4}}{x^2}\right)^{-2} =$

# *Scientific Notation*

✎ **Write each number in scientific notation.**

1) $0.113 =$

2) $0.02 =$

3) $2.5 =$

4) $20 =$

5) $60 =$

6) $0.004 =$

7) $78 =$

8) $1,600 =$

9) $1,450 =$

10) $91,000 =$

11) $2,000,000 =$

12) $0.0000006 =$

13) $354,000 =$

14) $0.000325 =$

15) $0.00023 =$

16) $56,000,000 =$

17) $21,000 =$

18) $78,000,000 =$

19) $0.0000022 =$

20) $0.00012 =$

✎ **Write each number in standard notation.**

21) $3 \times 10^{-1} =$

22) $5 \times 10^{-2} =$

23) $1.2 \times 10^{3} =$

24) $2 \times 10^{-4} =$

25) $1.5 \times 10^{-2} =$

26) $4 \times 10^{3} =$

27) $9 \times 10^{5} =$

28) $1.12 \times 10^{4} =$

29) $3 \times 10^{-5} =$

30) $8.3 \times 10^{-5} =$

# Answers of Worksheets – Chapter 7

## Multiplication Property of Exponents

1) $2^3$

2) $5^4$

3) $3^4$

4) $4^4$

5) $7^6$

6) $2^5$

7) $5^7$

8) $2x^2$

9) $x^5$

10) $x^8$

11) $x^6$

12) $36x^2$

13) $4x^4$

14) $3x^3$

15) $64x^{12}$

16) $2x^4$

17) $3x^5$

18) $2x^3$

19) $25x^8$

20) $4x^3y$

21) $3x^8y^2$

22) $x^5y^7$

23) $8x^5y^4$

24) $36x^5y^4$

25) $21x^6y^8$

26) $63x^3y^8$

27) $28x^4y^7$

28) $24x^7y^6$

29) $3x^4y^9$

30) $4x^5y^4$

31) $20x^6y^9$

32) $560x^{11}y^4$

## Zero and Negative Exponents

1) $1$

2) $\dfrac{1}{4}$

3) $0$

4) $1$

5) $\dfrac{1}{8}$

6) $\dfrac{1}{64}$

7) $\dfrac{1}{16}$

8) $\dfrac{1}{100}$

9) $\dfrac{1}{9}$

10) $\dfrac{1}{9}$

11) $\dfrac{1}{49}$

12) $\dfrac{1}{81}$

13) $\dfrac{1}{36}$

14) $\dfrac{1}{125}$

15) $\dfrac{1}{22}$

16) $\dfrac{1}{16}$

17) $\dfrac{1}{25}$

18) $\dfrac{1}{35}$

19) $\dfrac{1}{64}$

20) $\dfrac{1}{216}$

21) $\dfrac{1}{243}$

22) $\dfrac{1}{25}$

23) $\dfrac{1}{8}$

24) $\dfrac{1}{27}$

25) $\dfrac{1}{343}$

26) $\dfrac{1}{216}$

27) $\dfrac{1}{512}$

28) $\dfrac{1}{81}$

29) $\dfrac{1}{1,000}$

30) $\dfrac{1}{1,000,000,000}$

31) $2$

32) $4$

33) $9$

34) $\dfrac{9}{4}$

35) $125$

36) $\dfrac{16}{9}$

37) $\dfrac{25}{4}$

38) $256$

39) $\dfrac{125}{8}$

40) $\dfrac{49}{9}$

41) $\dfrac{216}{125}$

42) $\dfrac{81}{16}$

## Division Property of Exponents

1) $\frac{1}{2}$

2) $2^2$

3) $5^4$

4) $\frac{1}{3^4}$

5) $\frac{1}{x^2}$

6) $\frac{1}{3^2}$

7) $5^5$

8) $1$

9) $3$

10) $\frac{1}{2x^2}$

11) $\frac{3}{2x^2}$

12) $\frac{6}{7x^3}$

13) $\frac{4x^3}{3y^8}$

14) $\frac{5y^2}{x^5}$

15) $\frac{2x^3}{7}$

16) $\frac{4y^8}{x}$

17) $\frac{4}{5x^3y^9}$

18) $\frac{6}{5x^4}$

19) $\frac{16}{9x^4y}$

20) $\frac{1}{4}$

21) $\frac{2}{9x^3}$

## Powers of Products and Quotients

1) $4^4$

2) $6^6$

3) $2^{16}$

4) $4^{10}$

5) $3^{15}$

6) $5^{18}$

7) $2^{10}$

8) $2^{12}$

9) $121x^{10}$

10) $256x^8y^{16}$

11) $8x^{12}y^{12}$

12) $9x^4y^4$

13) $81x^{16}y^{12}$

14) $4x^{12}y^{16}$

15) $1,728x^{12}$

16) $8x^{45}$

17) $125x^{30}y^9$

18) $16x^{12}$

19) $225x^8$

20) $100x^{22}y^6$

21) $81x^{14}y^{10}$

22) $1,024x^{20}y^{30}$

23) $144x^2y^6$

24) $\frac{25}{x^2}$

25) $x^2y^2$

26) $\frac{25y^4}{x^{10}}$

27) $\frac{x^4}{y^4}$

28) $x^4y^2$

29) $\frac{4y^8}{x^4}$

30) $\frac{125}{y^6}$

## Negative Exponents and Negative Bases

1) $-\frac{1}{6}$

2) $-\frac{1}{25}$

3) $-\frac{1}{16}$

4) $-\frac{1}{x^3}$

5) $\frac{2}{x}$

6) $-\frac{4}{x^3}$

7) $-\frac{12}{x^5}$

8) $-\frac{5}{x^5y^3}$

9) $\frac{20}{x^4y}$

10) $\frac{14}{a^6b^7}$

11) $-\frac{12x^2}{y^3}$

12) $-25x^6$

13) $-2xa^4$

14) $9$

15) $\frac{16}{9}$

16) $-9a^7b^2$

17) $-5x^4$

18) $-\dfrac{b^2}{a^3}$

19) $-5x^3$

20) $-\dfrac{7bc^4}{9}$

21) $7a^4b^2$

22) $-\dfrac{p^3}{2n^2}$

23) $-\dfrac{4ac^2}{3b^2}$

24) $\dfrac{4c^2}{9a^2}$

25) $-\dfrac{27y^3z^3}{125x^3}$

26) $-\dfrac{4ac^2}{3b^2}$

27) $x^2$

28) $-81x^{12}$

29) $x^{12}$

## Writing Scientific Notation

1) $1.13 \times 10^{-1}$
2) $2 \times 10^{-2}$
3) $2.5 \times 10^{0}$
4) $2 \times 10^{1}$
5) $6 \times 10^{1}$
6) $4 \times 10^{-3}$
7) $7.8 \times 10^{1}$
8) $1.6 \times 10^{3}$
9) $1.45 \times 10^{3}$
10) $9.1 \times 10^{4}$

11) $2 \times 10^{6}$
12) $6 \times 10^{-7}$
13) $3.54 \times 10^{5}$
14) $3.25 \times 10^{-4}$
15) $2.3 \times 10^{-4}$
16) $5.6 \times 10^{7}$
17) $2.1 \times 10^{4}$
18) $7.8 \times 10^{7}$
19) $2.2 \times 10^{-6}$
20) $1.2 \times 10^{-4}$

21) $0.3$
22) $0.05$
23) $1,200$
24) $0.0002$
25) $0.015$
26) $4,000$
27) $900,000$
28) $11,200$
29) $0.00003$
30) $0.000083$

# Chapter 8:

# Polynomials

## Topics that you'll practice in this chapter:

✓ Writing Polynomials in Standard Form

✓ Simplifying Polynomials

✓ Adding and Subtracting Polynomials

✓ Multiplying Monomials

✓ Multiplying and Dividing Monomials

✓ Multiplying a Polynomial and a Monomial

✓ Multiplying Binomials

✓ Factoring Trinomials

✓ Operations with Polynomials

*Mathematics is the supreme judge; from its decisions there is no appeal.— Tobias Dantzig*

# Writing Polynomials in Standard Form

✎ *Write each polynomial in standard form.*

1) $9x - 7x =$

2) $-3 + 16x - 16x =$

3) $3x^2 - 5x^3 =$

4) $3 + 4x^3 - 3 =$

5) $2x^2 + 1x - 6x^3 =$

6) $-x^2 + 2x^3 =$

7) $2x + 4x^3 - 2x^2 =$

8) $-2x^2 + 4x - 6x^3 =$

9) $2x^2 + 2 - 5x =$

10) $12 - 7x + 9x^4 =$

11) $5x^2 + 13x - 2x^3 =$

12) $10 + 6x^2 - x^3 =$

13) $12x^2 - 7x + 9x^3 =$

14) $5x^4 - 3x^2 - 2x^3 =$

15) $-12 + 3x^2 - 6x^4 =$

16) $5x^2 - 9x^5 + 8x^3 - 11 =$

17) $4x^2 - 2x^5 + 14 - 7x^4 =$

18) $-x^2 + 2x - 5x^3 - 4x =$

19) $8x^5 + 11x^3 - 6x^5 - 8x^2 =$

20) $5x^2 - 12x^4 + 4x^2 + 5x^3 =$

21) $7x^3 - 6x^4 - 3x^2 + 22x^3 =$

22) $9x^2 + x^4 + 12x^3 - 5x^4 =$

23) $3x(2x + 5 - 2x^2) =$

24) $11x(x^5 + 2x^3) =$

25) $5x(3x^2 + 2x + 1) =$

26) $7x(3 - x + 6x^3) =$

27) $2x(3x^2 - 4x^4 + 3) =$

28) $6x(4x^5 + 7x^3 - 2) =$

29) $5x(3x^2 + 2x^3 + x) =$

30) $7x(3x - x^2 + 6x^4) =$

# Simplifying Polynomials

✎ *Simplify each expression.*

1) $5(2x - 10) =$

2) $2x(4x - 2) =$

3) $4x(5x - 3) =$

4) $3x(7x + 3) =$

5) $4x(8x - 4) =$

6) $5x(5x + 4) =$

7) $(2x - 3)(x - 4) =$

8) $(x - 5)(3x + 4) =$

9) $(x - 5)(x - 3) =$

10) $(3x + 8)(3x - 8) =$

11) $(3x - 8)(3x - 4) =$

12) $3x^2 + 3x^2 - 2x^3 =$

13) $2x - x^2 + 6x^3 + 4 =$

14) $5x + 2x^2 - 9x^3 =$

15) $7x^2 + 5x^4 - 2x^3 =$

16) $-3x^2 + 5x^3 + 6x^4 =$

17) $-8x^2 + 2x^3 - 10x^4 + 5x =$

18) $11 - 6x^2 + 5x^2 - 12x^3 + 22 =$

19) $2x^2 - 2x + 3x^3 + 12x - 22x =$

20) $11 - 4x^2 + 3x^2 - 7x^3 + 3 =$

21) $2x^5 - x^3 + 8x^2 - 2x^5 =$

22) $(2x^3 - 1) + (3x^3 - 2x^3) =$

23) $3(4x^4 - 4x^3 - 5x^4) =$

24) $-5(x^6 + 10) - 8(14 - x^6) =$

25) $3x^2 - 5x^3 - x + 10 - 2x^2 =$

26) $11 - 3x^2 + 2x^2 - 5x^3 + 7 =$

27) $(8x^2 - 3x) - (5x - 5 - 8x^2) =$

28) $3x^2 - 5x^3 - x(2x^2 + 4x) =$

29) $4x + 8x^3 - 4 - 3(x^3 - 2) =$

30) $12 + 2x^2 - (8x^3 - x^2 + 6x^3) =$

31) $-2(x^4 + 6) - 5(10 + x^4) =$

32) $(8x^3 - 2x) - (5x - 2x^3) =$

# Adding and Subtracting Polynomials

✎ *Add or subtract expressions.*

1) $(-x^2 - 2) + (2x^2 + 1) =$

2) $(2x^2 + 3) - (3 - 4x^2) =$

3) $(2x^3 + 3x^2) - (x^3 + 8) =$

4) $(4x^3 - x^2) + (3x^2 - 5x) =$

5) $(7x^3 + 9x) - (3x^3 + 2) =$

6) $(2x^3 - 2) + (2x^3 + 2) =$

7) $(4x^3 + 5) - (7 - 2x^3) =$

8) $(4x^2 + 2x^3) - (2x^3 + 5) =$

9) $(4x^2 - x) + (3x - 5x^2) =$

10) $(7x + 9) - (3x + 9) =$

11) $(4x^4 - 2x) - (6x - 2x^4) =$

12) $(12x - 4x^3) - (8x^3 + 6x) =$

13) $(2x^3 - 8x^2) - (5x^2 - 3x) =$

14) $(2x^2 - 6) + (9x^2 - 4x^3) =$

15) $(4x^3 + 3x^4) - (x^4 - 5x^3) =$

16) $(-2x^3 - 2x) + (6x - 2x^3) =$

17) $(2x - 4x^4) - (8x^4 + 3x) =$

18) $(2x - 8x^2) - (5x^4 - 3x^2) =$

19) $(2x^3 - 6) + (9x^3 - 4x^2) =$

20) $(4x^3 + 3x^4) - (x^4 - 5x^3) =$

21) $(-2x^2 + 10x^4 + x^3) + (4x^3 + 3x^4 + 8x^2) =$

22) $(3x^2 - 6x^5 - 2x) - (-2x^2 - 6x^5 + 2x) =$

23) $(5x + 9x^3 - 3x^5) + (8x^3 + 3x^5 - 2x) =$

24) $(3x^5 - 2x^4 - 4x) - (4x^2 + 10x^4 - 3x) =$

25) $(13x^2 - 6x^5 - 2x) - (-10x^2 - 11x^5 + 9x) =$

26) $(-12x^4 + 10x^5 + 2x^3) + (14x^3 + 23x^5 + 8x^4) =$

# *Multiplying Monomials*

✎ *Simplify each expression.*

1) $4u^9 \times (-2u^3) =$

2) $(-2p^7) \times (-3p^2) =$

3) $3xy^2z^3 \times 2z^2 =$

4) $5u^5t \times 3ut^2 =$

5) $(-9a^6) \times (-5a^2b^4) =$

6) $-2a^3b^2 \times 4a^2b =$

7) $2xy^2 \times x^2y^3 =$

8) $3p^2q^4 \times (-2pq^3) =$

9) $4s^5t^2 \times 4st^3 =$

10) $(-6x^3y^2) \times 3x^2y =$

11) $2xy^2z \times 4z^2 =$

12) $4xy \times x^2y =$

13) $4pq^3 \times (-2p^4q) =$

14) $8s^4t^2 \times st^5 =$

15) $12p^3 \times (-3p^4) =$

16) $(-4p^2q^3r) \times 6pq^2r^3 =$

17) $(-8a^4) \times -12a^6b) =$

18) $3u^4v^2 \times (-7u^2v^3) =$

19) $4u^3 \times (-2u) =$

20) $-6xy^2 \times 3x^2y =$

21) $12y^2z^3 \times (-y^2z) =$

22) $5a^2bc^2 \times 2abc^2 =$

23) $(-7p^3q^5) \times (-4p^2q^3) =$

24) $4u^5v^2 \times (-8u^3v^2) =$

25) $12y^3z^4 \times (-y^6z) =$

26) $(-4pq^5r^3) \times 6p^2q^4r =$

27) $5ab^4c^2 \times 2a^5bc^2 =$

28) $2x^4yz^3 \times 3x^2y^4z^2 =$

# *Multiplying and Dividing Monomials*

✎ *Simplify each expression.*

1) $(2x^2)(x^3) =$

2) $(3x^4)(2x^4) =$

3) $(6x^5)(2x^2) =$

4) $(4x^3)(3x^5) =$

5) $(15x^4)(3x^9) =$

6) $(2yx^2)(3y^2x^3) =$

7) $(2x^2y)(x^2y^3) =$

8) $(-2x^3y^4)(3x^3y^2) =$

9) $(-5x^3y^2)(-2x^4y^5) =$

10) $(9x^5y)(-3x^3y^3) =$

11) $(8x^7y^2)(6x^5y^4) =$

12) $(7x^4y^6)(4x^3y^4) =$

13) $(12x^2y^9)(7x^9y^{12}) =$

14) $(6x^2y^5)(5x^3y^2) =$

15) $(9x^2y^9)(4x^{10}y^9) =$

16) $(-10x^4y^8)(2x^9y^5) =$

17) $\dfrac{4x^2y^3}{xy^2} =$

18) $\dfrac{2x^4y^3}{2x^3y} =$

19) $\dfrac{8x^2y^2}{4x} =$

20) $\dfrac{6x^3y^4}{2x^2y^3} =$

21) $\dfrac{12^{\ 6}y^8}{4x^4y^2} =$

22) $\dfrac{26^{\ 9}y^5}{2x^3y^4} =$

23) $\dfrac{80^{\ 12}y^9}{10^{\ 6}y^7} =$

24) $\dfrac{95^{\ 18}y^7}{5x^9y^2} =$

25) $\dfrac{200x^3y^8}{40x^3y^7} =$

26) $\dfrac{-15x^{17}y^{13}}{3x^6y^9} =$

27) $\dfrac{-64x^8y^{10}}{8x^3y^7} =$

# Multiplying a Polynomial and a Monomial

✎ *Find each product.*

1) $x(x + 3) =$

2) $8(2 - x) =$

3) $2x(2x + 1) =$

4) $x(-x + 3) =$

5) $3x(3x - 2) =$

6) $5(3x - 6y) =$

7) $8x(7x - 4) =$

8) $3x(9x + 2y) =$

9) $6x(x + 2y) =$

10) $9x(2x + 4y) =$

11) $12x(3x + 9) =$

12) $11x(2x - 11y) =$

13) $2x(6x - 6y) =$

14) $2x(3x - 6y + 3) =$

15) $5x(3x^2 + 2y^2) =$

16) $13x(4x + 8y) =$

17) $5(2x^2 - 9y^2) =$

18) $3x(-2x^2y + 3y) =$

19) $-2(2x^2 - 2xy + 2) =$

20) $3(x^2 - 4xy - 8) =$

21) $2x(2x^2 - 3xy + 2x) =$

22) $-x(-x^2 - 5x + 4xy) =$

23) $9(x^2 + xy - 8y^2) =$

24) $3x(2x^2 - 3x + 8) =$

25) $20(2x^2 - 8x - 5) =$

26) $x^2(-x^2 + 3x + 7) =$

27) $x^3(x^2 + 12 - 2x) =$

28) $6x^3(3x^2 - 2x + 2) =$

29) $8x^2(3x^2 - 5xy + 7y^2) =$

30) $2x^2(3x^2 - 5x + 12) =$

31) $2x^3(2x^2 + 5x - 4) =$

32) $5x(6x^2 - 5xy + 2y^2) =$

# *Multiplying Binomials*

✎ *Find each product.*

1) $(x + 2)(x + 2) =$

2) $(x - 3)(x + 2) =$

3) $(x - 2)(x - 4) =$

4) $(x + 3)(x + 2) =$

5) $(x - 4)(x - 5) =$

6) $(x + 5)(x + 2) =$

7) $(x - 6)(x + 3) =$

8) $(x - 8)(x - 4) =$

9) $(x + 2)(x + 8) =$

10) $(x - 2)(x + 4) =$

11) $(x + 4)(x + 4) =$

12) $(x + 5)(x + 5) =$

13) $(x - 3)(x + 3) =$

14) $(x - 2)(x + 2) =$

15) $(x + 3)(x + 3) =$

16) $(x + 4)(x + 6) =$

17) $(x - 7)(x + 7) =$

18) $(x - 7)(x + 2) =$

19) $(2x + 2)(x + 3) =$

20) $(2x - 3)(2x + 4) =$

21) $(x - 8)(2x + 8) =$

22) $(x - 7)(x - 6) =$

23) $(x - 8)(x + 8) =$

24) $(3x - 2)(4x + 2) =$

25) $(2x - 5)(x + 7) =$

26) $(5x - 4)(3x + 3) =$

27) $(6x + 9)(4x + 9) =$

28) $(2x - 6)(5x + 6) =$

29) $(x + 4)(4x - 8) =$

30) $(6x - 4)(6x + 4) =$

31) $(3x + 3)(3x - 4) =$

32) $(x^2 + 2)(x^2 - 2) =$

# *Factoring Trinomials*

✍ *Factor each trinomial.*

1) $x^2 + 8x + 15 =$

2) $x^2 - 5x + 6 =$

3) $x^2 + 6x + 8 =$

4) $x^2 - 6x + 8 =$

5) $x^2 - 8x + 16 =$

6) $x^2 - 7x + 12 =$

7) $x^2 + 11x + 18 =$

8) $x^2 + 2x - 24 =$

9) $x^2 + 4x - 12 =$

10) $x^2 - 10x + 9 =$

11) $x^2 + 5x - 14 =$

12) $x^2 - 6x - 27 =$

13) $x^2 - 11x - 42 =$

14) $x^2 + 22x + 121 =$

15) $6x^2 + x - 12 =$

16) $x^2 - 17x + 30 =$

17) $3x^2 + 11x - 4 =$

18) $10x^2 + 33x - 7 =$

19) $x^2 + 24x + 144 =$

20) $8x^2 + 10x - 3 =$

✍ *Solve each problem.*

21) The area of a rectangle is $x^2 + 2x - 24$. If the width of rectangle is $x - 4$, what is its length? _____

22) The area of a parallelogram is $8x^2 + 2x - 6$ and its height is $2x + 2$. What is the base of the parallelogram? _____

23) The area of a rectangle is $18x^2 + 9x - 2$. If the width of the rectangle is $6x - 1$, what is its length? _____

# Operations with Polynomials

✏️ *Find each product.*

1) $9(6x + 2) =$ _____

2) $8(3x + 7) =$ _____

3) $5(6x - 1) =$ _____

4) $-3(8x - 3) =$ _____

5) $3x^2(6x - 5) =$ _____

6) $5x^2(7x - 2) =$ _____

7) $6x^3(-3x + 4) =$ _____

8) $-7x^4(2x - 4) =$ _____

9) $8(x^2 + 2x - 3) =$ _____

10) $4(4x^2 - 2x + 1) =$ _____

11) $2(3x^2 + 2x - 2) =$ _____

12) $8x(5x^2 + 3x + 8) =$ _____

13) $(9x + 1)(3x - 1) =$ _____

14) $(4x + 5)(6x - 5) =$ _____

15) $(7x + 3)(5x - 6) =$ _____

16) $(3x - 4)(3x + 8) =$ _____

✏️ *Solve each problem.*

17) The measures of two sides of a triangle are $(2x + 3y)$ and $(5x - 2y)$. If the perimeter of the triangle is $(12x + 5y)$, what is the measure of the third side? _____

18) The height of a triangle is $(4x + 5)$ and its base is $(2x - 2)$. What is the area of the triangle? _____

19) One side of a square is $(6x + 9)$. What is the area of the square? _____

20) The length of a rectangle is $(5x - 2y)$ and its width is $(12x + 2y)$. What is the perimeter of the rectangle? _____

21) The side of a cube measures $(x + 2)$. What is the volume of the cube? _____

22) If the perimeter of a rectangle is $(16x + 8y)$ and its width is $(2x + y)$, what is the length of the rectangle? _____

# *Answers of Worksheets – Chapter 8*

### *Writing Polynomials in Standard Form*

1) $2x$
2) $-3$
3) $-5x^3 + 3x^3$
4) $4x^3$
5) $-6x^3 + 2x^3 + x$
6) $2x^3 - x^2$
7) $4x^3 - 2x^2 + 2x$
8) $-6x^3 - 2x^2 + 4x$
9) $2x^2 - 5x + 2$
10) $9x^4 - 7x + 12$
11) $-2x^3 + 5x^2 + 13x$
12) $-x^3 + 6x^2 + 10$
13) $9x^3 + 12x^2 - 7x$
14) $5x^4 - 2x^3 - 3x^2$
15) $-6x^4 + 3x^2 - 12$
16) $-9x^5 + 8x^3 + 5x^2 - 11$

17) $-2x^5 - 7x^4 + 4x^2 + 14$
18) $-5x^3 - x^2 - 2x$
19) $2x^5 + 11x^3 - 8x^2$
20) $-12x^4 + 5x^3 + 9x^2$
21) $-6x^4 + 29x^3 - 3x^2$
22) $-4x^4 + 12x^3 + 9x^2$
23) $-6x^3 + 6x^2 + 15x$
24) $11x^6 + 22x^4$
25) $15x^3 + 10x^2 + 5x$
26) $42x^4 - 7x^2 + 21x$
27) $-8x^5 + 6x^3 + 6x$
28) $24x^6 + 42x^4 - 12x$
29) $10x^4 + 15x^3 + 5x^2$
30) $42x^5 - 7x^3 + 21x^2$

### *Simplifying Polynomials*

1) $10x - 50$
2) $8x^2 - 4x$
3) $20x^2 - 12x$
4) $21x^2 + 9x$
5) $32x^2 - 16x$
6) $25x^2 + 20x$
7) $2x^2 - 11x + 12$
8) $3x^2 - 11x - 20$
9) $x^2 - 8x + 15$
10) $9x^2 - 64$
11) $9x^2 - 36x + 32$
12) $-2x^3 + 6x^2$
13) $6x^3 - x^2 + 2x + 4$
14) $-9x^3 + 2x^2 + 5x$
15) $5x^4 - 2x^3 + 7x^2$
16) $6x^4 + 5x^3 - 3x^2$

17) $-10x^4 + 2x^3 - 8x^2 + 5x$
18) $-12x^3 - x^2 + 33$
19) $3x^3 + 2x^2 - 12x$
20) $-7x^3 - x^2 + 14$
21) $-x^3 + 8x^2$
22) $3x^3 - 1$
23) $-3x^4 - 12x^3$
24) $3x^6 - 162$
25) $-5x^3 + x^2 - x + 10$
26) $-5x^3 - x^2 + 18$
27) $16x^2 - 8x + 5$
28) $-5x^3 - x^2$
29) $5x^3 + 4x + 2$
30) $-14x^3 + 3x^2 + 12$
31) $-7x^4 - 62$
32) $10x^3 - 7x$

## Adding and Subtracting Polynomials

1) $x^2 - 1$
2) $6x^2$
3) $x^3 + 3x^2 - 8$
4) $4x^3 + 2x^2 - 5x$
5) $4x^3 + 9x - 2$
6) $4x^3$
7) $6x^3 - 2$
8) $4x^2 - 5$
9) $-x^2 + 2x$
10) $4x$
11) $6x^4 - 8x$
12) $-12x^3 + 6x$
13) $2x^3 - 13x^2 + 3x$

14) $-4x^3 + 11x^2 - 6$
15) $2x^4 + 9x^3$
16) $-4x^3 + 4x$
17) $-12x^4 - x$
18) $-5x^4 - 5x^2 + 2x$
19) $11x^3 - 4x^2 - 6$
20) $2x^4 + 9x^3$
21) $13x^4 + 5x^3 + 6x^2$
22) $5x^2 - 4x$
23) $17x^3 + 3x$
24) $3x^5 - 12x^4 - 4x^2 - x$
25) $5x^5 + 23x^2 - 11x$
26) $33x^5 - 4x^4 + 16x^3$

## Multiplying Monomials

1) $-8u^{12}$
2) $6p^9$
3) $6xy^2z^5$
4) $15u^6t^3$
5) $45a^8b^4$
6) $-8a^5b^3$
7) $2x^3y^5$
8) $-6p^3q^7$
9) $16s^6t^5$
10) $-18x^5y^3$
11) $8xy^2z^3$

12) $4x^3y^2$
13) $-8p^5q^4$
14) $8s^5t^7$
15) $-36p^7$
16) $-24p^3q^4r^4$
17) $96a^{10}b$
18) $-21u^6v^5$
19) $-8u^4$

20) $-18x^3y^3$
21) $-12y^4z^4$
22) $10a^3b^2c^4$
23) $28p^5q^8$
24) $-32u^8v^4$
25) $-12y^9z^5$
26) $-24p^3q^9r^4$
27) $10a^6b^5c^4$
28) $6x^6y^5z^5$

## Multiplying and Dividing Monomials

1) $2x^5$
2) $6x^8$
3) $12x^7$
4) $12x^8$
5) $45x^{13}$
6) $6x^5y^3$
7) $2x^4y^4$
8) $-6x^6y^6$

9) $10x^7y^7$
10) $-27x^8y^4$
11) $48x^{12}y^6$
12) $28x^7y^{10}$
13) $84x^{11}y^{21}$
14) $30x^5y^7$
15) $36x^{12}y^{18}$
16) $-20x^{13}y^{13}$

17) $4xy$
18) $xy^2$
19) $2xy$
20) $3xy$
21) $3x^2y^6$
22) $13x^6y$
23) $8x^6y^2$
24) $19x^9y^5$

25) $5y$            26) $-5x^{11}y^4$            27) $-8x^5y^3$

## Multiplying a Polynomial and a Monomial

1) $x^2 + 3x$
2) $-8x + 16$
3) $4x^2 + 2x$
4) $-x^2 + 3x$
5) $9x^2 - 6x$
6) $15x - 30y$
7) $56x^2 - 32x$
8) $27x^2 + 6xy$
9) $6x^2 + 12xy$
10) $18x^2 + 36xy$
11) $36x^2 + 108x$
12) $22x^2 - 121xy$
13) $12x^2 - 12xy$
14) $6x^2 - 12xy + 6x$
15) $15x^3 + 10xy^2$
16) $52x^2 + 104xy$
17) $10x^2 - 45y^2$

18) $-6x^3y + 9xy$
19) $-4x^2 + 4xy - 4$
20) $3x^2 - 12xy - 24$
21) $4x^3 - 6x^2y + 4x^2$
22) $x^3 + 5x^2 - 4x^2y$
23) $9x^2 + 9xy - 72y^2$
24) $6x^3 - 9x^2 + 24x$
25) $40x^2 - 160x - 100$
26) $-x^4 + 3x^3 + 7x^2$
27) $x^5 - 2x^4 + 12x^3$
28) $18x^5 - 12x^4 + 12x^3$
29) $24x^4 - 40x^3y + 56x^2y^2$
30) $6x^4 - 10x^3 + 24x^2$
31) $4x^5 + 10x^4 - 8x^3$
32) $30x^3 - 25x^2y + 10xy^2$

## Multiplying Binomials

1) $x^2 + 4x + 4$
2) $x^2 - x - 6$
3) $x^2 - 6x + 8$
4) $x^2 + 5x + 6$
5) $x^2 - 9x + 20$
6) $x^2 + 7x + 10$
7) $x^2 - 3x - 18$
8) $x^2 - 12x + 32$
9) $x^2 + 10x + 16$
10) $x^2 + 2x - 8$
11) $x^2 + 8x + 6$
12) $x^2 + 10x + 25$
13) $x^2 - 9$
14) $x^2 - 4$
15) $x^2 + 6x + 9$
16) $x^2 + 10x + 24$

17) $x^2 - 49$
18) $x^2 - 5x - 14$
19) $2x^2 + 8x + 6$
20) $4x^2 + 2x - 12$
21) $2x^2 - 8x - 64$
22) $x^2 - 13x + 42$
23) $x^2 - 64$
24) $12x^2 - 2x - 4$
25) $2x^2 + 9x - 35$
26) $15x^2 + 3x - 12$
27) $24x^2 + 90x + 81$
28) $10x^2 - 18x - 36$
29) $4x^2 + 8x - 32$
30) $36x^2 - 16$
31) $9x^2 - 3x - 12$
32) $x^4 - 4$

## Factoring Trinomials

1) $(x + 3)(x + 5)$

2) $(x - 2)(x - 3)$

3) $(x + 4)(x + 2)$

4) $(x - 2)(x - 4)$

5) $(x - 4)(x - 4)$

6) $(x - 3)(x - 4)$

7) $(x + 2)(x + 9)$

8) $(x + 6)(x - 4)$

9) $(x - 2)(x + 6)$

10) $(x - 1)(x - 9)$

11) $(x - 2)(x + 7)$

12) $(x - 9)(x + 3)$

13) $(x + 3)(x - 14)$

14) $(x + 11)(x + 11)$

15) $(2x + 3)(3x - 4)$

16) $(x - 15)(x - 2)$

17) $(3x - 1)(x + 4)$

18) $(5x - 1)(2x + 7)$

19) $(x + 12)(x + 12)$

20) $(4x - 1)(2x + 3)$

21) $(x + 6)$

22) $(4x - 3)$

23) $(3x + 2)$

## Operations with Polynomials

1) $54x + 18$

2) $24x + 56$

3) $30x - 5$

4) $-24x + 9$

5) $18x^3 - 15x^2$

6) $35x^3 - 10x^2$

7) $-18x^4 + 24x^3$

8) $-14x^5 + 28x^4$

9) $8x^2 + 16x - 24$

10) $16x^2 - 8x + 4$

11) $6x^2 + 4x - 4$

12) $40x^3 + 24x^2 + 64x$

13) $27x^2 - 6x - 1$

14) $24x^2 + 10x - 25$

15) $35x^2 + 27x - 18$

16) $9x^2 + 12x - 32$

17) $(5x + 4y)$

18) $8x^2 + 2x - 10$

19) $36x^2 + 108x + 81$

20) $34x$

21) $x^3 + 6x^2 + 12x + 6$

22) $(6x + 3y)$

# Chapter 9:

# Functions Operations

### Topics that you'll practice in this chapter:

✓ Evaluating Function

✓ Adding and Subtracting Functions

✓ Multiplying and Dividing Functions

✓ Composition of Functions

*Mathematics is like checkers in being suitable for the young, not too difficult, amusing, and*

*without peril to the state. — Plato*

# *Evaluating Function*

🖎 **Write each of following in function notation.**

1) $h = 2x + 5$

2) $k = 12a - 9$

3) $d = 22t$

4) $y = 2x - 6$

5) $m = 25n - 120$

6) $c = p^2 + 5p + 5$

🖎 **Evaluate each function.**

7) $f(x) = x - 2$, find $f(1)$

8) $g(x) = 2x + 3$, find $f(2)$

9) $h(x) = x + 8$, find $f(5)$

10) $f(x) = -x + 5$, find $f(4)$

11) $f(a) = 3a - 3$, find $f(-1)$

12) $h(x) = 12 - 2x$, find $f(6)$

13) $g(n) = 4n - 2$, find $f(-2)$

14) $f(x) = -5x + 3$, find $f(3)$

15) $k(n) = -8 + 4n$, find $f(2)$

16) $f(x) = -7x + 4$, find $f(-3)$

17) $g(n) = 10n - 3$, find $g(6)$

18) $g(n) = 8n + 4$, find $g(1)$

19) $h(x) = 4x - 22$, find $h(2)$

20) $h(n) = n^2 + 2$, find $h(3)$

21) $h(n) = n^2 - 7$, find $h(2)$

22) $h(n) = n^2 + 4$, find $h(-4)$

23) $h(n) = n^2 - 10$, find $h(5)$

24) $h(n) = -2n^2 - 6n$, find $h(2)$

25) $g(n) = 3n^2 + 2n$, find $g(2)$

26) $h(a) = -11a + 5$, find $h(2a)$

27) $k(a) = 7a + 3$, find $k(a - 2)$

28) $h(x) = 3x + 5$, find $h(6x)$

29) $h(x) = x^2 + 1$, find $h(\frac{x}{4})$

30) $h(x) = x^3 + 8$, find $h(3x)$

# Adding and Subtracting Functions

✎ *Perform the indicated operation.*

1) $f(x) = 2x + 4$
   $g(x) = x + 3$
   Find $(f - g)(1)$

7) $f(x) = 4x - 3$
   $g(x) = x^3 + 2x$
   Find $(f - g)(4)$

2) $g(a) = 2a - 1$
   $f(a) = -a - 4$
   Find $(g - f)(-1)$

8) $h(n) = 4n + 5$
   $g(n) = 3n + 4$
   Find $(h - g)(n)$

3) $h(t) = 2t + 1$
   $g(t) = 2t + 2$
   Find $(h - g)(t)$

9) $g(x) = -x^2 - 1 - 2x$
   $f(x) = 5 + x$
   Find $(g - f)(x)$

4) $g(a) = -3a - 3$
   $f(a) = a^2 + 5$
   Find $(g - f)(a)$

10) $g(t) = 2t + 5$
    $f(t) = -t^2 + 5$
    Find $(g + f)(t)$

5) $g(x) = 2x - 5$
   $h(x) = 4x + 5$
   Find $g(3) - h(3)$

11) $f(x) = 3x + 2$
    $g(x) = -2x^2 + x$
    Find $(f + g)(x)$

6) $h(3) = 3x + 3$
   $g(x) = -4x + 1$
   Find $(h + g)(10)$

12) $f(x) = -2x^2 - 4x$
    $g(x) = 4x + 3$
    Find $(f + g)(x^2)$

# Multiplying and Dividing Functions

✎ *Perform the indicated operation.*

1) $g(x) = -x - 2$

    $f(x) = 2x + 1$

    Find $(g.f)(2)$

2) $f(x) = 3x$

    $h(x) = -2x + 5$

    Find $(f.h)(-1)$

3) $g(a) = 2a - 1$

    $h(a) = 3a - 3$

    Find $(g.h)(-4)$

4) $f(x) = x + 4$

    $h(x) = 5x - 2$

    Find $\left(\frac{f}{h}\right)(2)$

5) $f(x) = 2a^2$

    $g(x) = -5 + 3a$

    Find $\left(\frac{f}{g}\right)(2)$

6) $g(a) = 3a + 2$

    $f(a) = 2a - 4$

    Find $\left(\frac{g}{f}\right)(3)$

7) $g(t) = t^2 + 3$

    $h(t) - 4t - 3$

    Find $(g.h)(-1)$

8) $g(n) = n^2 + 4 + 2n$

    $h(n) = -3n + 2$

    Find $(g.h)(1)$

9) $g(a) = 2a^3 - 5a + 2$

    $f(a) = a^3 - 4$

    Find $\left(\frac{g}{f}\right)(2)$

10) $g(x) = -2x^2 + 14 - 2x$

    $f(x) = x^2 + 5$

    Find $(g.f)(4)$

11) $f(x) = 2x^3 - 5x^2$

    $g(x) = 2x - 1$

    Find $(f.g)(x)$

12) $f(x) = 3x - 1$

    $g(x) = x^2 - x$

    Find $\left(\frac{f}{g}\right)(x)$

# Composition of Functions

✍ **Using** f(x) = x + 2 **and** g(x) = 4x, **find:**

1) $f\big(g(1)\big) =$

2) $f\big(g(-2)\big) =$

3) $g\big(f(-1)\big) =$

4) $g\big(f(3)\big) =$

5) $f\big(g(2)\big) =$

6) $g\big(f(5)\big) =$

✍ **Using** f(x) = 5x + 4 **and** g(x) = x − 3, **find:**

7) $g\big(f(-3)\big) =$

8) $g\big(f(4)\big) =$

9) $f\big(g(6)\big) =$

10) $f\big(f(8)\big) =$

11) $g\big(f(-7)\big) =$

12) $g\big(f(x)\big) =$

✍ **Using** f(x) = 6x + 2 **and** g(x) = x − 5, **find:**

13) $g\big(f(-2)\big) =$

14) $f\big(f(4)\big) =$

15) $f\big(g(7)\big) =$

16) $f\big(f(2)\big) =$

17) $g\big(f(3)\big) =$

18) $g\big(g(x)\big) =$

✍ **Using** f(x) = 7x + 4 **and** g(x) = 2x − 4, **find:**

19) $f\big(g(-3)\big) =$

20) $g\big(f(-2)\big) =$

21) $f\big(g(3)\big) =$

22) $f\big(f(3)\big) =$

23) $g\big(f(4)\big) =$

24) $g\big(g(5)\big) =$

# *Answers of Worksheets – Chapter 9*

## *Evaluating Function*

1) $h(x) = 2x + 5$
2) $k(a) = 12a - 9$
3) $d(t) = 22t$
4) $f(x) = 2x - 6$
5) $m(n) = 25n - 120$
6) $c(p) = p^2 + 5p + 5$
7) $-1$
8) $7$
9) $13$
10) $1$
11) $-6$

12) $0$
13) $-10$
14) $-12$
15) $0$
16) $25$
17) $57$
18) $12$
19) $-14$
20) $11$
21) $-3$
22) $20$

23) $15$
24) $-20$
25) $16$
26) $-22a + 5$
27) $7a - 11$
28) $18x + 5$
29) $\frac{1}{16}x^2 + 1$
30) $27x^3 + 8$

## *Adding and Subtracting Functions*

1) $2$
2) $0$
3) $-1$
4) $-a^2 - 3a - 8$
5) $-16$
6) $-6$

7) $-59$
8) $n + 1$
9) $-x^2 - 3x - 6$
10) $-t^2 + 2t + 10$
11) $-2x^2 + 4x + 2$
12) $-2x^6 + 3$

## *Multiplying and Dividing Functions*

1) $-20$
2) $-21$
3) $135$
4) $\frac{6}{8} = \frac{3}{4}$
5) $8$
6) $\frac{11}{2}$

7) $-28$
8) $-7$
9) $2$
10) $-546$
11) $4x^4 - 12x^3 + 5x^2$
12) $\frac{3x-1}{x^2-x}$

## Composition of Functions

| | | |
|---|---|---|
| 1) 6 | 9) 19 | 17) 15 |
| 2) $-6$ | 10) 41 | 18) $x - 10$ |
| 3) 4 | 11) $-31$ | 19) $-66$ |
| 4) 20 | 12) $5x + 1$ | 20) $-24$ |
| 5) 10 | 13) $-15$ | 21) 18 |
| 6) 28 | 14) 21 | 22) 179 |
| 7) $-14$ | 15) 14 | 23) 60 |
| 8) 24 | 16) 86 | 24) 8 |

# Chapter 10:

# Quadratic

**Topics that you'll practice in this chapter:**

- ✓ Graphing Quadratic Functions

- ✓ Solving Quadratic Equations

- ✓ Use the Quadratic Formula and the Discriminant

- ✓ Solve Quadratic Inequalities

*It's fine to work on any problem, so long as it generates interesting mathematics along the way*

*— even if you don't solve it at the end of the day." – Andrew Wiles*

# Solving Quadratic Equations

✎ *Solve each equation by factoring or using the quadratic formula.*

1) $(x + 2)(x - 7) = 0$

2) $(x + 3)(x + 5) = 0$

3) $(x - 9)(x + 4) = 0$

4) $(x - 7)(x - 5) = 0$

5) $(x + 4)(x + 8) = 0$

6) $(5x + 7)(x + 4) = 0$

7) $(2x + 5)(4x + 3) = 0$

8) $(3x + 4)(x + 2) = 0$

9) $(6x + 3)(2x + 4) = 0$

10) $(9x + 3)(x + 6) = 0$

11) $x^2 = 2x$

12) $x^2 - 6 = x$

13) $2x^2 + 4 = 6x$

14) $-x^2 - 6 = 5x$

15) $x^2 + 8x = 9$

16) $x^2 + 10x = 24$

17) $x^2 + 7x = -10$

18) $x^2 + 12x = -32$

19) $x^2 + 11x = -28$

20) $x^2 + x - 20 = 2x$

21) $x^2 + 8x = -15$

22) $7x^2 - 14x = -7$

23) $10x^2 = 27x - 18$

24) $7x^2 - 6x + 3 = 3$

25) $2x^2 - 14 = -3x$

26) $10x^2 - 26x = -12$

27) $15x^2 + 80 = -80x$

28) $x^2 + 15x = -56$

29) $6x^2 - 18x - 18 = 6$

30) $2x^2 + 6x - 24 = 12$

31) $2x^2 - 22x + 38 = -10$

32) $-4x^2 - 8x - 3 = -3 - 5x^2$

# Quadratic Formula and the Discriminant

✎ *Find the value of the discriminant of each quadratic equation.*

1) $x(x-1)=0$

2) $x^2+2x-1=0$

3) $x^2+3x+5=0$

4) $x^2-x+4=0$

5) $x^2+x-2=0$

6) $x^2+4x-6=0$

7) $x^2+5x+2=0$

8) $2x^2-2x-7=0$

9) $2x^2+3x+9=0$

10) $2x^2+5x-4=0$

11) $5x^2+x-2=0$

12) $-3x^2-6x+2=0$

13) $-4x^2-4x+5=0$

14) $-2x^2-x-1=0$

15) $6x^2-2x-3=0$

16) $-5x^2-3x+9=0$

17) $4x^2+5x-4=0$

18) $8x^2-9x=0$

19) $3x^2-5x+1=0$

20) $5x^2+6x+4=0$

✎ *Find the discriminant of each quadratic equation then state the number of real and imaginary solutions.*

21) $-x^2-9=6x$

22) $4x^2=8x-4$

23) $-4x^2-4x=6$

24) $8x^2-6x+3=5x^2$

25) $-9x^2=-8x+8$

26) $9x^2+6x+6=5$

27) $9x^2-3x-8=-10$

28) $-2x^2-8x-14=-6$

# Quadratic Inequalities

✎ *Solve each quadratic inequality.*

1) $x^2 - 1 < 0$

2) $-x^2 - 5x + 6 > 0$

3) $x^2 - 5x - 6 < 0$

4) $x^2 + 4x - 5 > 0$

5) $x^2 - 2x - 3 \geq 0$

6) $x^2 > 5x + 6$

7) $-x^2 - 12x - 11 \leq 0$

8) $x^2 - 2x - 8 \geq 0$

9) $x^2 - 5x - 6 \geq 0$

10) $x^2 + 7x + 10 < 0$

11) $x^2 + 9x + 20 > 0$

12) $x^2 - 8x + 16 > 0$

13) $x^2 - 8x + 12 \leq 0$

14) $x^2 - 11x + 30 \leq 0$

15) $x^2 - 12x + 27 \geq 0$

16) $x^2 - 16x + 64 \geq 0$

17) $x^2 - 36 \leq 0$

18) $x^2 - 13x + 36 \geq 0$

19) $x^2 + 15x + 36 \leq 0$

20) $4x^2 - 6x - 9 > x^2$

21) $5x^2 - 15x + 10 < 0$

22) $3x^2 - 5x \geq 4x^2 + 6$

23) $4x^2 - 12 > 3x^2 + x$

24) $x^2 - 2x \geq x^2 - 6x + 12$

25) $2x^2 + 2x - 8 > x^2$

26) $4x^2 + 20x - 11 < 0$

27) $-9x^2 + 29x - 6 \geq 0$

28) $-8x^2 + 6x - 1 \leq 0$

29) $12x^2 + 10x - 12 > 0$

30) $18x^2 + 23x + 5 \leq 0$

31) $17x^2 + 15x - 2 \geq 0$

32) $3x^2 + 7x \leq 5x^2 + 3x - 6$

# *Graphing Quadratic Functions*

✍ *Sketch the graph of each function. Identify the vertex and axis of symmetry.*

1) $y = 3(x + 1)^2 + 2$

2) $y = -(x - 2)^2 - 4$

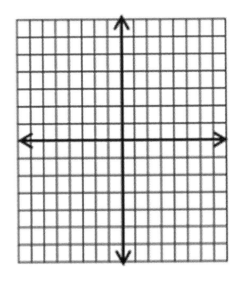
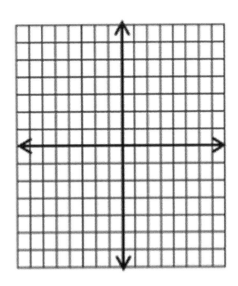

3) $y = 2(x - 3)^2 + 8$

4) $y = x^2 - 8x + 19$

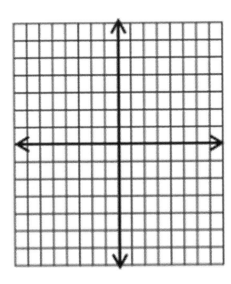
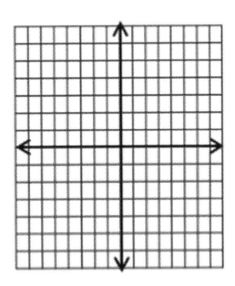

# *Answers of Worksheets – Chapter 10*

## *Solving quadratic equations*

1) $\{-2, 7\}$
2) $\{-3, -5\}$
3) $\{9, -4\}$
4) $\{7, 5\}$
5) $\{-4, -8\}$
6) $\{-\frac{7}{5}, -4\}$
7) $\{-\frac{5}{2}, -\frac{3}{4}\}$
8) $\{-\frac{4}{3}, -2\}$
9) $\{-\frac{1}{2}, -2\}$
10) $\{-\frac{1}{3}, -6\}$

11) $\{2, 0\}$
12) $\{3, -2\}$
13) $\{2, 1\}$
14) $\{-3, -2\}$
15) $\{1, -9\}$
16) $\{2, -12\}$
17) $\{-2, -5\}$
18) $\{-4, -8\}$
19) $\{-4, -7\}$
20) $\{5, -4\}$
21) $\{-5, -3\}$
22) $\{1\}$

23) $\{\frac{6}{5}, \frac{3}{2}\}$
24) $\{\frac{6}{7}, 0\}$
25) $\{-\frac{7}{2}, 2\}$
26) $\{\frac{3}{5}, 2\}$
27) $\{-\frac{4}{3}, -4\}$
28) $\{-8, -7\}$
29) $\{4, -1\}$
30) $\{3, -6\}$
31) $\{3, 8\}$
32) $\{8, 0\}$

## *Quadratic formula and the discriminant*

1) 1
2) 8
3) $-11$
4) $-15$
5) 9
6) 40
7) 17
8) 60
9) $-45$
10) 57

11) 41
12) 60
13) 96
14) $-7$
15) 76
16) 189
17) 89
18) 81
19) 13
20) $-44$

21) $0, one\ real\ solution$
22) $0, one\ real\ solution$
23) $-80, no\ solution$
24) $0, one\ real\ solution$
25) $-224, no\ solution$
26) $0, one\ real\ solution$
27) $-63, solution$
28) $0, one\ real\ solution$

## *Solve quadratic inequalities*

1) $-1 < x < 1$
2) $-6 < x < 1$
3) $-1 < x < 6$
4) $x < -5\ or\ x > 1$
5) $x \le -1\ or\ x \ge 3$
6) $x < -1\ or\ x > 6$
7) $x \le -11\ or\ x \ge -1$
8) $x \le -2\ or\ x \ge 4$
9) $x \le -1\ or\ x \ge 6$
10) $-5 < x < -2$
11) $x < -5\ or\ x > -4$
12) $x < 4\ or\ x > 4$

13) $2 \le x \le 6$
14) $5 \le x \le 6$
15) $x \le 3\ or\ x \ge 9$
16) $all\ real\ numbers$
17) $-6 \le x \le 6$
18) $x \le 4\ or\ x \ge 9$
19) $-12 \le x \le -3$
20) $x < -1\ or\ x > 3$
21) $1 < x < 2$
22) $-3 \le x \le -2$
23) $x < -3\ or\ x > 4$
24) $x \ge 3$

25) $x < -4\ or\ x > 2$
26) $-\frac{11}{2} < x < \frac{1}{2}$
27) $\frac{2}{9} \le x \le 3$
28) $x \le \frac{1}{4}\ or\ x \ge \frac{1}{2}$
29) $x < -1.5\ or\ x > \frac{2}{3}$
30) $-1 \le x \le -\frac{5}{18}$
31) $x \le -1\ or\ x \ge \frac{2}{17}$
32) $x \le -1\ or\ x \ge 3$

## Graphing quadratic functions

1) $(-1, 2), x = -1$

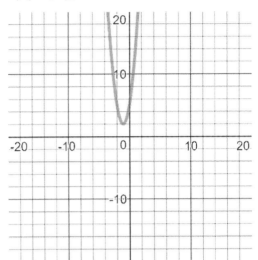

2) $(2, -4), x = 2$

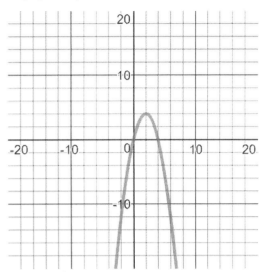

3) $(3, 8), x = 3$

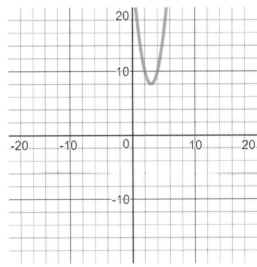

4) $(4, 3), x = 4$

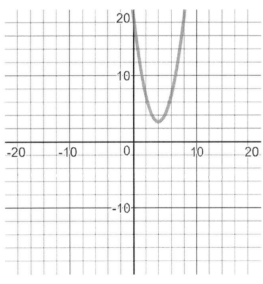

# Chapter 11:

# Radical Expressions

## Topics that you'll practice in this chapter:

- ✓ Simplifying Radical Expressions
- ✓ Simplifying Radical Expressions Involving Fractions
- ✓ Multiplying Radical Expressions
- ✓ Adding and Subtracting Radical Expressions
- ✓ Domain and Range of Radical Functions
- ✓ Solving Radical Equations

*Mathematics is an independent world created out of pure intelligence.*

*— William Woods Worth*

# *Simplifying Radical Expressions*

✎ **Simplify.**

1) $\sqrt{35x^2} =$

2) $\sqrt{90x^2} =$

3) $\sqrt[3]{8a} =$

4) $\sqrt{100x^3} =$

5) $\sqrt{125a} =$

6) $\sqrt[3]{88w^3} =$

7) $\sqrt{80x} =$

8) $\sqrt{216v} =$

9) $\sqrt[3]{125x}$

10) $\sqrt{64x^5} -$

11) $\sqrt{4x^2} =$

12) $\sqrt[3]{54a^2}$

13) $\sqrt{405} =$

14) $\sqrt{512p^3} =$

15) $\sqrt{216m^4} =$

16) $\sqrt{264x^3y^3} =$

17) $\sqrt{49x^3y^3} =$

18) $\sqrt{16a^4b^3} =$

19) $\sqrt{20x^3y^3} =$

20) $\sqrt[3]{216yx^3} =$

21) $3\sqrt{75x^2} =$

22) $5\sqrt{80x^2} =$

23) $\sqrt[3]{256x^2y^3} =$

24) $\sqrt[3]{343x^4y^2} =$

25) $4\sqrt{125a} =$

26) $\sqrt[3]{625xy} =$

27) $2\sqrt{8x^2y^3r} =$

28) $4\sqrt{36x^2y^3z^4} =$

29) $2\sqrt[3]{512x^3y^4} =$

30) $5\sqrt{64a^2b^3c^5} =$

31) $2\sqrt[3]{125x^6y^{12}} =$

# Multiplying Radical Expressions

✍ *Simplify.*

1) $\sqrt{5} \times \sqrt{5} =$

2) $\sqrt{5} \times \sqrt{10} =$

3) $\sqrt{2} \times \sqrt{18} =$

4) $\sqrt{14} \times \sqrt{21} =$

5) $\sqrt{5} \times -4\sqrt{20} =$

6) $3\sqrt{12} \times \sqrt{6} =$

7) $5\sqrt{42} \times \sqrt{3} =$

8) $\sqrt{3} \times -\sqrt{25} =$

9) $\sqrt{99} \times \sqrt{48} =$

10) $5\sqrt{45} \times 3\sqrt{176} =$

11) $\sqrt{12}(3 + \sqrt{3}) =$

12) $\sqrt{23x^2} \times \sqrt{23x} =$

13) $-5\sqrt{12} \times - \sqrt{3} =$

14) $2\sqrt{20x^2} \times \sqrt{5x^2} =$

15) $\sqrt{12x^2} \times \sqrt{2x^3} =$

16) $-12\sqrt{7x} \times \sqrt{5x^3} =$

17) $-5\sqrt{9x^3} \times 6\sqrt{3x^2} =$

18) $-2\sqrt{12}(3 + \sqrt{12}) =$

19) $\sqrt{18x}(4 - \sqrt{6x}) =$

20) $\sqrt{3x}(6\sqrt{x^3} + \sqrt{27}) =$

21) $\sqrt{15r}(5 + \sqrt{5}) =$

22) $-5\sqrt{3x} \times 4\sqrt{6x^3} =$

23) $-2\sqrt{18x} \times 4\sqrt{2x}$

24) $-3\sqrt{5v^2}(-3\sqrt{15v}) =$

25) $(\sqrt{5} - \sqrt{3})(\sqrt{5} + \sqrt{3}) =$

26) $(-4\sqrt{6} + 2)(\sqrt{6} - 5) =$

27) $(2 - 2\sqrt{3})(-2 + \sqrt{3}) =$

28) $(11 - 4\sqrt{5})(6 - \sqrt{5}) =$

29) $(-2 - \sqrt{3x})(3 + \sqrt{3x}) =$

30) $(-2 + 3\sqrt{2r})(-2 + \sqrt{2r}) =$

31) $(-4\sqrt{2n} + 2)(-2\sqrt{2} - 4) =$

32) $(-1 + 2\sqrt{3})(2 - 3\sqrt{3x}) =$

# *Simplifying Radical Expressions Involving Fractions*

✎ **Simplify.**

1) $\dfrac{\sqrt{5}}{\sqrt{3}} =$

2) $\dfrac{\sqrt{8}}{\sqrt{100}} =$

3) $\dfrac{\sqrt{2}}{2\sqrt{3}} =$

4) $\dfrac{4}{\sqrt{5}} =$

5) $\dfrac{2\sqrt{5r}}{\sqrt{m^3}} =$

6) $\dfrac{8\sqrt{3}}{\sqrt{k}} =$

7) $\dfrac{6\sqrt{14x^2}}{2\sqrt{18}} =$

8) $\dfrac{\sqrt{7x^2y^2}}{\sqrt{5x^3y^2}} =$

9) $\dfrac{1}{1+\sqrt{2}} =$

10) $\dfrac{1-5\sqrt{a}}{\sqrt{11a}} =$

11) $\dfrac{\sqrt{a}}{\sqrt{a}+\sqrt{b}} =$

12) $\dfrac{1+\sqrt{2}}{3+\sqrt{5}} =$

13) $\dfrac{2+\sqrt{5}}{6-\sqrt{3}} =$

14) $\dfrac{5}{-3-3\sqrt{3}}$

15) $\dfrac{2}{3+\sqrt{5}} =$

16) $\dfrac{\sqrt{7}-\sqrt{3}}{\sqrt{3}-\sqrt{7}} =$

17) $\dfrac{\sqrt{7}+\sqrt{5}}{\sqrt{5}+\sqrt{2}} =$

18) $\dfrac{3\sqrt{2}-\sqrt{7}}{4\sqrt{2}+\sqrt{5}} =$

19) $\dfrac{\sqrt{5}+2\sqrt{2}}{4-\sqrt{5}} =$

20) $\dfrac{5\sqrt{3}-3\sqrt{2}}{3\sqrt{2}-2\sqrt{3}} =$

21) $\dfrac{\sqrt{8a^5b^3}}{\sqrt{2a^2}} =$

22) $\dfrac{6\sqrt{45x^3}}{3\sqrt{5x}} =$

# Adding and Subtracting Radical Expressions

✎ **Simplify.**

1) $\sqrt{3} + \sqrt{27} =$

2) $3\sqrt{8} + 3\sqrt{2} =$

3) $4\sqrt{3} - 2\sqrt{12} =$

4) $3\sqrt{18} - 2\sqrt{2} =$

5) $2\sqrt{45} - 2\sqrt{5} =$

6) $-\sqrt{12} - 5\sqrt{3} =$

7) $-4\sqrt{2} - 5\sqrt{32} =$

8) $5\sqrt{10} + 2\sqrt{40} =$

9) $4\sqrt{12} - 3\sqrt{27} =$

10) $-3\sqrt{2} + 4\sqrt{18} =$

11) $-10\sqrt{7} + 6\sqrt{28} =$

12) $5\sqrt{3} - \sqrt{27} =$

13) $-\sqrt{12} + 3\sqrt{3} =$

14) $-3\sqrt{6} - \sqrt{54} =$

15) $3\sqrt{8} + 3\sqrt{2} =$

16) $2\sqrt{12} - 3\sqrt{27} =$

17) $\sqrt{50} - \sqrt{32} =$

18) $4\sqrt{8} - 6\sqrt{2} =$

19) $-4\sqrt{12} + 12\sqrt{108} =$

20) $2\sqrt{45} - 2\sqrt{5} =$

21) $7\sqrt{18} - 3\sqrt{2} =$

22) $-12\sqrt{35} + 7\sqrt{140} =$

23) $-6\sqrt{19} - 3\sqrt{76} =$

24) $-\sqrt{54x} - 3\sqrt{6x} =$

25) $\sqrt{5y^2} + y\sqrt{45} =$

26) $\sqrt{8mn^2} + 2n\sqrt{18m} =$

27) $-8\sqrt{27a} - 5\sqrt{3a} =$

28) $-4\sqrt{7ab} - \sqrt{28ab} =$

29) $\sqrt{27a^2b} + a\sqrt{12b} =$

30) $3\sqrt{6a^3} - 2\sqrt{24a^3} + 2a\sqrt{54a} =$

# *Domain and Range of Radical Functions*

✎ *Identify the domain and range of each function.*

1) $y = \sqrt{x + 2} - 3$

2) $y = \sqrt[3]{x - 1} - 1$

3) $y = \sqrt{x - 2} + 5$

4) $y = \sqrt[3]{(x + 1)} - 4$

5) $y = 3\sqrt{3x + 6} + 5$

6) $y = \sqrt[3]{(2x - 1)} - 4$

7) $y = 6\sqrt{3x^2 + 6} + 5$

8) $y = \sqrt[3]{(2x^2 - 2)} - 4$

9) $y = 4\sqrt{4x^3 + 32} - 1$

10) $y = \sqrt[3]{(4x + 8)} - 2x$

11) $y = 7\sqrt{-2(2x + 4)} + 1$

12) $y = \sqrt[5]{(4x^2 - 5)} - 2$

13) $y = 2x\sqrt{5x^4 + 6} - 2x$

14) $y = 6\sqrt[3]{(8x^6 + 2x + 8)} - 2$

✎ *Sketch the graph of each function.*

5) $y = \sqrt{x} + 8$

6) $y = 2\sqrt{x} - 4$

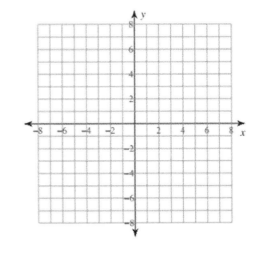

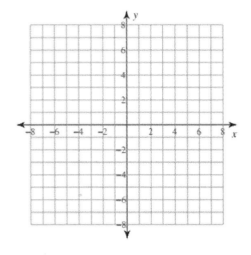

# Solving Radical Equations

✍ *Solve each equation. Remember to check for extraneous solutions.*

1) $\sqrt{a} = 5$

2) $\sqrt{v} = 3$

3) $\sqrt{r} = 4$

4) $2 = 4\sqrt{x}$

5) $\sqrt{x+1} = 9$

6) $1 = \sqrt{x-5}$

7) $6 = \sqrt{r-2}$

8) $\sqrt{x-6} = 8$

9) $5 = \sqrt{x-3}$

10) $\sqrt{m+8} = 8$

11) $10\sqrt{9a} = 60$

12) $5\sqrt{3x} = 15$

13) $1 = \sqrt{3x-5}$

14) $\sqrt{12-x} = x$

15) $\sqrt{r+3} - 1 = 7$

16) $-12 = -6\sqrt{r+4}$

17) $20 = 2\sqrt{36v}$

18) $x = \sqrt{42-x}$

19) $\sqrt{110-a} = a$

20) $\sqrt{2n-12} = 2$

21) $\sqrt{3r-5} = r-3$

22) $\sqrt{-16+10x} = x$

23) $\sqrt{3x+12} = \sqrt{x+8}$

24) $\sqrt{v} = \sqrt{2v-6}$

25) $\sqrt{11-x} = \sqrt{x-7}$

26) $\sqrt{m+8} = \sqrt{3m+8}$

27) $\sqrt{2r+40} = \sqrt{-16-2r}$

28) $\sqrt{k+3} = \sqrt{1-k}$

29) $-10\sqrt{x-10} = -60$

30) $\sqrt{72-x} = \sqrt{\dfrac{x}{5}}$

# *Answers of Worksheets – Chapter 11*

### *Simplifying radical expressions*

1) $x\sqrt{35}$

2) $3x\sqrt{10}$

3) $2\sqrt[3]{a}$

4) $10x\sqrt{x}$

5) $5\sqrt{5a}$

6) $2w\sqrt[3]{11}$

7) $4\sqrt{5x}$

8) $6\sqrt{6v}$

9) $5\sqrt[3]{x}$

10) $8x^2\sqrt{x}$

11) $2x$

12) $3\sqrt[3]{2a^2}$

13) $9\sqrt{5}$

14) $16p\sqrt{2p}$

15) $6m^2\sqrt{6}$

16) $2x.\,y\sqrt{66xy}$

17) $7xy\sqrt{xy}$

18) $4a^2b\sqrt{b}$

19) $2xy\sqrt{5xy}$

20) $6x\sqrt[3]{y}$

21) $15x\sqrt{3}$

22) $20x\sqrt{5}$

23) $16y\sqrt[3]{x^2}$

24) $7x\sqrt[3]{xy^2}$

25) $20\sqrt{5a}$

26) $5\sqrt[3]{5xy}$

27) $4xy\sqrt{2yr}$

28) $24\,x\,yz^2\sqrt{y}$

29) $16xy\sqrt[3]{y}$

30) $40abc^2\sqrt{bc}$

31) $10x^2y^4$

### *Multiplying radical expressions*

1) $5$

2) $5\sqrt{2}$

3) $6$

4) $7\sqrt{6}$

5) $-40$

6) $18\sqrt{2}$

7) $15\sqrt{14}$

8) $-5\sqrt{3}$

9) $12\sqrt{33}$

10) $180\sqrt{55}$

11) $6\sqrt{3}+6$

12) $23x\sqrt{x}$

13) $30$

14) $20x^2$

15) $2x\sqrt{6x}$

16) $-12x^2\sqrt{35}$

17) $-90x^2\sqrt{3x}$

18) $-12\sqrt{3}-24$

19) $6\sqrt{2x}-6x\sqrt{3}$

20) $54x^2$

21) $5\sqrt{15r}+3\sqrt{5r}$

22) $-60x^2\sqrt{2}$

23) $-48x$

24) $45v\sqrt{3v}$

25) $2$

26) $22\sqrt{3} - 34$

27) $6\sqrt{3} - 10$

28) $86 - 35\sqrt{5}$

29) $-3x - 5\sqrt{3x} - 6$

30) $12r - 8\sqrt{2r} + 4$

31) $16\sqrt{n} + 16\sqrt{2n} - 4\sqrt{2} - 8$

32) $-2 + 3\sqrt{3x} + 4\sqrt{3} - 18\sqrt{x}$

## Simplifying radical expressions involving fractions

1) $\dfrac{\sqrt{15}}{3}$

2) $\dfrac{\sqrt{2}}{5}$

3) $\dfrac{\sqrt{6}}{6}$

4) $\dfrac{4\sqrt{5}}{5}$

5) $\dfrac{2\sqrt{5mr}}{m^2}$

6) $\dfrac{8\sqrt{3k}}{k}$

7) $\sqrt{7x}$

8) $\dfrac{\sqrt{35x}}{5x}$

9) $-1 + \sqrt{2}$

10) $\dfrac{\sqrt{11} - 5a\sqrt{11}}{11a}$

11) $\dfrac{a - \sqrt{ab}}{a - b}$

12) $\dfrac{3 - \sqrt{5} + 3\sqrt{2} - \sqrt{10}}{4}$

13) $\dfrac{12 + 2\sqrt{3} + 6\sqrt{5} + \sqrt{15}}{33}$

14) $\dfrac{5 - 5\sqrt{5}}{6}$

15) $-3 + \sqrt{5}$

16) $-1$

17) $\dfrac{\sqrt{35} - \sqrt{14} + 5 - \sqrt{10}}{3}$

18) $\dfrac{24 - 3\sqrt{10} - 4\sqrt{14} + \sqrt{35}}{27}$

19) $\dfrac{4\sqrt{5} + 5 + 8\sqrt{2} + 2\sqrt{10}}{11}$

20) $\dfrac{3\sqrt{6} + 4}{2}$

21) $2a^2\sqrt{b}$

22) $6x$

## Adding and subtracting radical expressions

1) $4\sqrt{3}$

2) $9\sqrt{2}$

3) $0$

4) $7\sqrt{2}$

5) $4\sqrt{5}$

6) $-7\sqrt{3}$

7) $-24\sqrt{2}$

8) $9\sqrt{10}$

9) $-\sqrt{3}$

10) $9\sqrt{2}$

11) $2\sqrt{7}$

12) $2\sqrt{3}$

13) $\sqrt{3}$

14) $0$

15) $9\sqrt{2}$

16) $-5\sqrt{3}$

17) $\sqrt{2}$

18) $2\sqrt{2}$

19) $64\sqrt{3}$

20) $4\sqrt{5}$

21) $18\sqrt{2}$

22) $2\sqrt{35}$

23) $-12\sqrt{19}$

24) $-6\sqrt{6x}$

25) $4y\sqrt{5}$

26) $8n\sqrt{2m}$

27) $-29\sqrt{3a}$

28) $-8\sqrt{7ab}$

29) $5a\sqrt{3b}$

30) $5a\sqrt{6a}$

## Domain and range of radical functions

1) domain: $x \geq -2$
   range: $y \geq -3$

2) domain: {all real numbers}
   range: {all real numbers}

3) domain: $x \geq 2$
   range: $y \geq 5$

4) domain: {all real numbers}
   range: {all real numbers}

5) domain: $x \geq -2$
   range: $y \geq 5$

6) domain: {all real numbers}
   range: {all real numbers}

7) domain: {all real numbers}
   range: {all real numbers}

8) domain: {all real numbers}
   range: {all real numbers}

9) domain: $x \geq -2$
   range: $y \geq -1$

10) domain: {all real numbers}
    range: {all real numbers}

11) domain: $x \leq -2$
    range: $y \geq 1$

12) domain: {all real numbers}
    range: {all real numbers}

13) domain: {all real numbers}
    range: {all real numbers}

14) domain: {all real numbers}
    range: {all real numbers}

5)

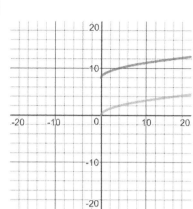

6)

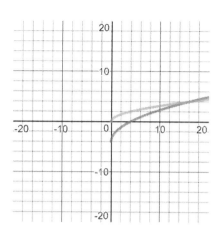

## Solving radical equations

1) $\{25\}$

2) $\{9\}$

3) $\{16\}$

4) $\{\frac{1}{4}\}$

5) $\{80\}$

6) $\{6\}$

7) $\{38\}$

8) $\{70\}$

9) $\{28\}$

10) $\{56\}$

11) $\{4\}$

12) $\{3\}$

13) $\{2\}$

14) $\{3\}$

15) $\{61\}$

16) $\{0\}$

17) $\{\frac{25}{9}\}$

18) $\{6\}$

19) $\{10\}$

20) $\{8\}$

21) $\{4\}$

22) $\{2, 8\}$

23) $\{-2\}$

24) $\{6\}$

25) $\{9\}$

26) $\{0\}$

27) $\{-14\}$

28) $\{-1\}$

29) $\{46\}$

30) $\{60\}$

# Chapter 12:

# Geometry and Solid Figures

## Topics that you'll practice in this chapter:

✓ Angles

✓ Pythagorean Relationship

✓ Triangles

✓ Polygons

✓ Trapezoids

✓ Circles

✓ Cubes

✓ Rectangular Prism

✓ Cylinder

✓ Pyramids and Cone

*Mathematics is, as it were, a sensuous logic, and relates to philosophy as do the arts, music, and plastic art to poetry. — K. Shegel*

# *Angles*

✎ **What is the value of x in the following figures?**

1)

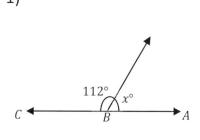

2)

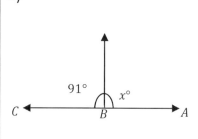

3)

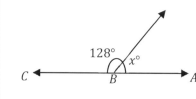

4)

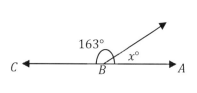

5)

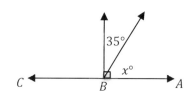

6)

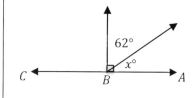

✎ **Solve.**

7) Two complementary angles have equal measures.  What is the measure of each angle?
_____

8) The measure of an angle is two third the measure of its supplement.  What is the measure of the angle? _____

9) Two angles are complementary and the measure of one angle is 24 less than the other.  What is the measure of the bigger angle? _____

10) Two angles are complementary.  The measure of one angle is half the measure of the other.  What is the measure of the smaller angle? _____

11) Two supplementary angles are given.  The measure of one angle is 50° less than the measure of the other.  What does the bigger angle measure? _____

# Pythagorean Relationship

✎ **Do the following lengths form a right triangle?**

1)
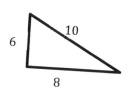

2)
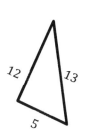

3)
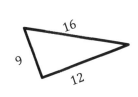

4)
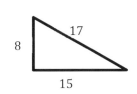

5)

6)
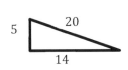

7)
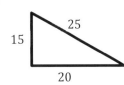

8)
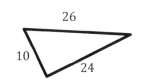

✎ **Find the missing side?**

9)
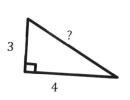

10)

11)
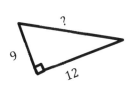

12)
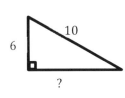

13)

14)
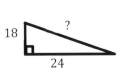

15)
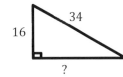

16)
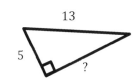

# Triangles

✍ *Find the measure of the unknown angle in each triangle.*

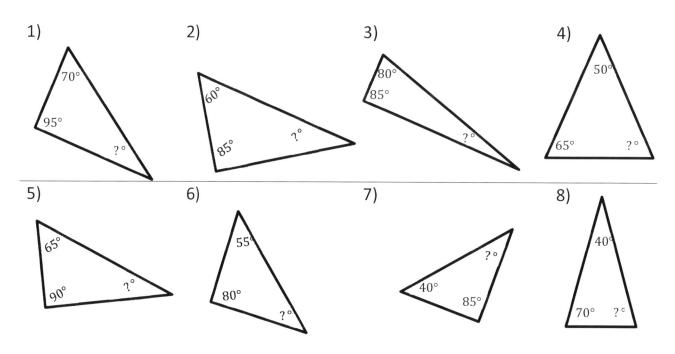

1)    2)    3)    4)

✍ *Find area of each triangle.*

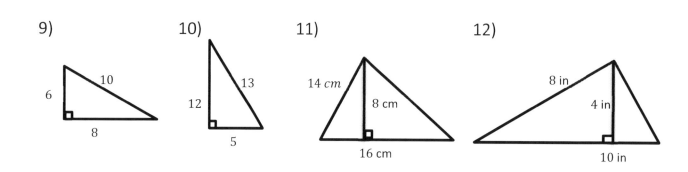

9)    10)    11)    12)

# *Polygons*

🖎 *Find the perimeter of each shape.*

1)

12 ft

12 ft       12 ft

12 ft

2)

10 in

8 in       8 in

10 in

3)

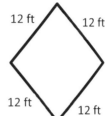

12 ft   12 ft

12 ft   12 ft

4) Square

14 cm

5) Regular hexagon

5 m

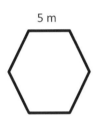

6)

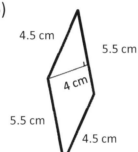

4.5 cm

5.5 cm

4 cm

5.5 cm

4.5 cm

7) Parallelogram

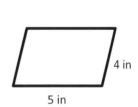

4 in

5 in

8) Square

6 m

🖎 *Find the area of each shape.*

9) Parallelogram

6 m

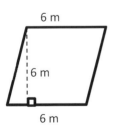

6 m

6 m

10) Rectangle

10 in

8 in

11) Rectangle

7 km

5 km

12) Square

7 in

# *Trapezoids*

 *Find the area of each trapezoid.*

1)

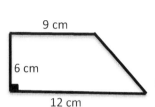

9 cm
6 cm
12 cm

2)

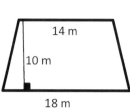

14 m
10 m
18 m

3)

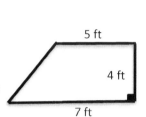

5 ft
4 ft
7 ft

4)

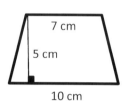

7 cm
5 cm
10 cm

5)

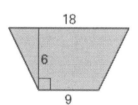

18
6
9

6)

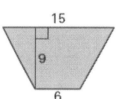

15
9
6

7)

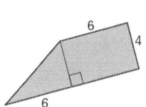

6
4
6

8)

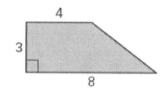

4
3
8

 *Solve.*

9) A trapezoid has an area of 60 cm$^2$ and its height is 6 cm and one base is 8 cm. What is the other base length? _____

10) If a trapezoid has an area of 65 ft$^2$ and the lengths of the bases are 12 ft and 14 ft, find the height. _____

11) If a trapezoid has an area of 180 m$^2$ and its height is 12 m and one base is 20 m, find the other base length. _____

12) The area of a trapezoid is 625 ft$^2$ and its height is 25 ft. If one base of the trapezoid is 15 ft, what is the other base length? _____

# *Circles*

 *Find the area of each circle.* ($\pi = 3.14$)

1)          2)          3)          4)          5)          6)

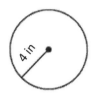                                        

7)          8)          9)          10)          11)          12)

 *Complete the table below.* ($\pi = 3.14$)

|  | Radius | Diameter | Circumference | Area |
|---|---|---|---|---|
| **Circle 1** | 4 inches | 8 inches | 25.12 inches | 50.24 square inches |
| **Circle 2** |  | 12 meters |  |  |
| **Circle 3** |  |  |  | 12.56 square ft |
| **Circle 4** |  |  | 18.84 miles |  |
| **Circle 5** |  | 5 kilometers |  |  |
| **Circle 6** | 6 centimeters |  |  |  |
| **Circle 7** |  | 8 feet |  |  |
| **Circle 8** |  |  |  | 28.26 square meters |
| **Circle 9** |  |  | 43.96 inches |  |
| **Circle 10** | 5 feet |  |  |  |

# Cubes

✎ *Find the volume of each cube.*

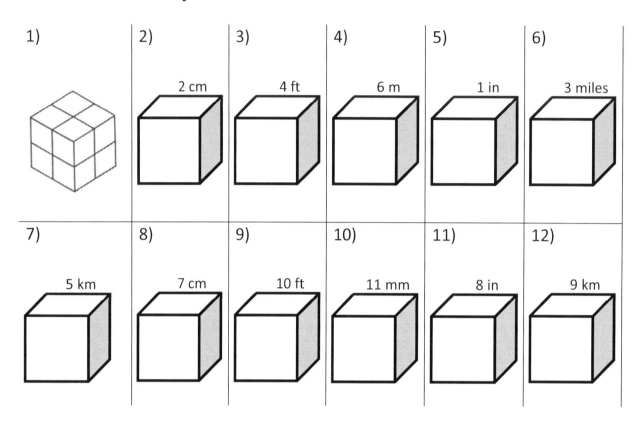

1)

2) 2 cm

3) 4 ft

4) 6 m

5) 1 in

6) 3 miles

7) 5 km

8) 7 cm

9) 10 ft

10) 11 mm

11) 8 in

12) 9 km

✎ *Find the surface area of each cube.*

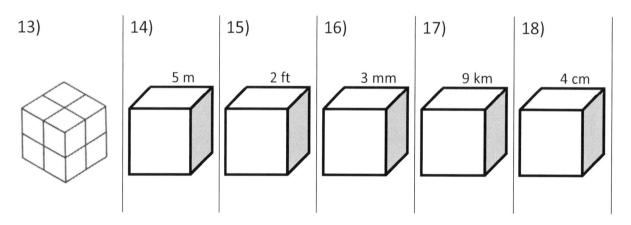

13)

14) 5 m

15) 2 ft

16) 3 mm

17) 9 km

18) 4 cm

# *Rectangular Prism*

✎ *Find the volume of each Rectangular Prism.*

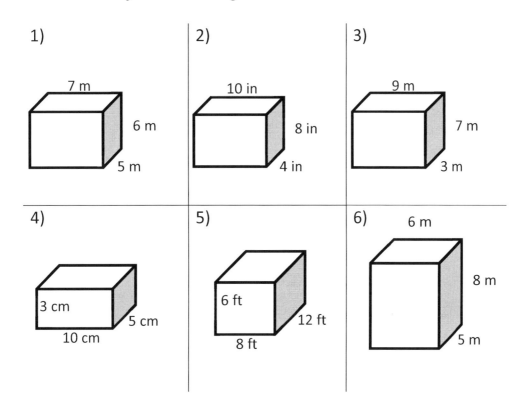

1)  7 m  6 m  5 m

2)  10 in  8 in  4 in

3)  9 m  7 m  3 m

4)  3 cm  5 cm  10 cm

5)  6 ft  12 ft  8 ft

6)  6 m  8 m  5 m

✎ *Find the surface area of each Rectangular Prism.*

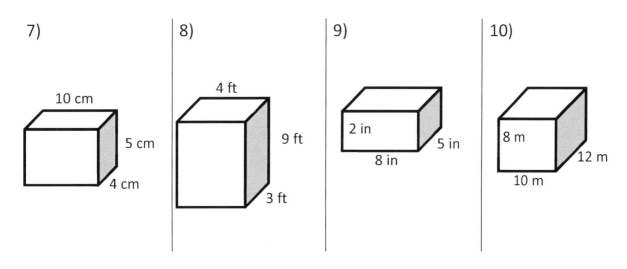

7)  10 cm  5 cm  4 cm

8)  4 ft  9 ft  3 ft

9)  2 in  5 in  8 in

10)  8 m  12 m  10 m

# *Cylinder*

✏ *Find the volume of each Cylinder. Round your answer to the nearest tenth.* (π = 3.14)

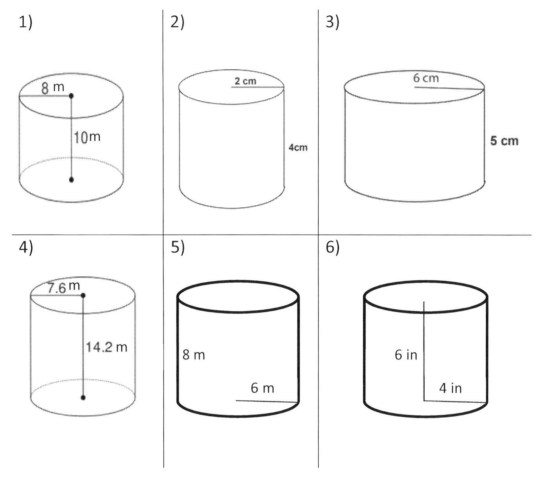

1) 8 m, 10m

2) 2 cm, 4cm

3) 6 cm, 5 cm

4) 7.6 m, 14.2 m

5) 8 m, 6 m

6) 6 in, 4 in

✏ *Find the surface area of each Cylinder.* (π = 3.14)

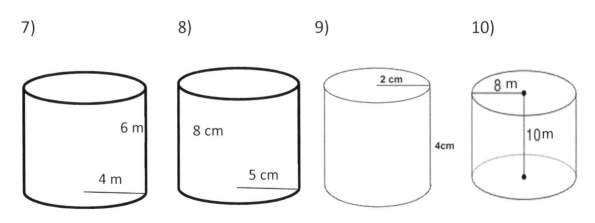

7) 6 m, 4 m

8) 8 cm, 5 cm

9) 2 cm, 4cm

10) 8 m, 10m

# *Pyramids and Cone*

✎ *Find the volume of each Pyramid and Cone.* ($\pi = 3.14$)

1)

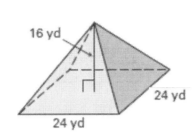

2)

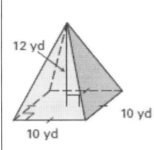

3)

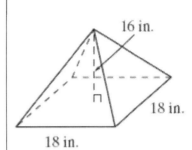

4)

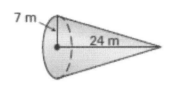

5)

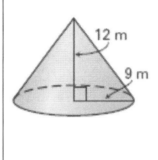

6)

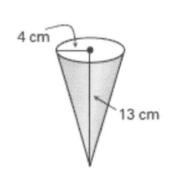

✎ *Find the surface area of each Pyramid and Cone.* ($\pi = 3.14$)

7)

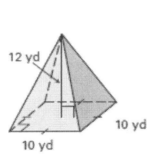

8)

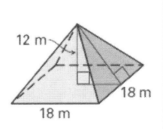

9)

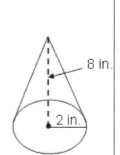

10)

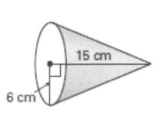

# *Answers of Worksheets – Chapter 12*

### *Angles*

1)  68°
2)  89°
3)  52°
4)  17°

5)  55°
6)  28°
7)  45°
8)  72°

9)  57°
10) 30°
11) 115°

### *Pythagorean Relationship*

1) Yes
2) Yes
3) No
4) Yes
5) No
6) No

7) Yes
8) Yes
9) 5
10) 17
11) 15
12) 8

13) 5
14) 30
15) 30
16) 12

### *Triangles*

1)  15°
2)  35°
3)  15°
4)  65°

5)  25°
6)  45°
7)  55°
8)  70°

9)  24 *square unites*
10) 30 *square unites*
11) 64 *square unites*
12) 20 *square unites*

### *Polygons*

1)  48 *ft*
2)  36 *in*
3)  48 *ft*
4)  56 *cm*
5)  30 *m*

6)  20 *cm*
7)  18 *in*
8)  24 *m*
9)  36 $m^2$

10) 80 $in^2$
11) 35 $km^2$
12) 49 $in^2$

### *Trapezoids*

1)  63 $cm^2$
2)  160 $m^2$
3)  24 $ft^2$
4)  42.5 $cm^2$

5)  81
6)  94.5
7)  36
8)  18
9)  12 *cm*

10) 5 *ft*
11) 10 *m*
12) 35 *ft*

### *Circles*

1)  50.24 $in^2$
2)  113.04 $cm^2$

3)  12.56 $ft^2$
4)  314 $m^2$

5)  28.26 $cm^2$
6)  200.96 $miles^2$

7)  $12.56\ in^2$

8)  $3.14\ ft^2$

9)  $50.24\ m^2$

10) $78.5\ cm^2$

11) $113.04\ miles^2$

12) $19.63\ ft^2$

|  | Radius | Diameter | Circumference | Area |
|---|---|---|---|---|
| Circle 1 | 4 inches | 8 inches | 25.12 inches | 50.24 square inches |
| Circle 2 | 6 meters | 12 meters | 37.68 meters | 113.04 meters |
| Circle 3 | 2 square ft | 4 square ft | 12.56 square ft | 12.56 square ft |
| Circle 4 | 3 miles | 6 miles | 18.84 miles | 28.26 miles |
| Circle 5 | 2.5 kilometers | 5 kilometers | 15.7 kilometers | 19.63 kilometers |
| Circle 6 | 6 centimeters | 12 centimeters | 37.68 centimeters | 113.04 centimeters |
| Circle 7 | 4 feet | 8 feet | 25.12 feet | 50.24 feet |
| Circle 8 | 3 square meters | 6 square meters | 18.84 square meters | 28.26 square meters |
| Circle 9 | 7 inches | 14 inches | 43.96 inches | 153.86 inches |
| Circle 10 | 5 feet | 10 feet | 31.4 feet | 78.5 feet |

## Cubes

1)  8
2)  $8\ cm^3$
3)  $64\ ft^3$
4)  $216\ m^3$
5)  $1\ in^3$
6)  $27\ miles^3$

7)  $125\ km^3$
8)  $343\ cm^3$
9)  $1,000\ ft^3$
10) $1,331\ mm^3$
11) $512\ in^3$
12) $729\ km^3$

13) 24
14) $150\ m^2$
15) $24\ ft^2$
16) $54\ mm^2$
17) $486\ km^2$
18) $96\ cm^2$

## Rectangular Prism

1)  $210\ m^3$
2)  $320\ in^3$
3)  $189\ m^3$
4)  $150\ cm^3$

5)  $576\ ft^3$
6)  $240\ m^3$
7)  $220\ cm^2$
8)  $150\ ft^2$

9)  $132\ in2$
10) $592\ m^2$

## Cylinder

1)  $2,009.6\ m^3$
2)  $50.24\ cm^3$
3)  $565.2\ cm^3$
4)  $2,575.4\ m^3$

5)  $904.3\ m^3$
6)  $301.4\ in^3$
7)  $251.2\ m^2$
8)  $408.2\ cm^2$

9)  $75.4\ cm^2$
10) $904.3\ m^2$

## Pyramids and Cone

1)  $3,072\ yd^3$
2)  $400\ yd^3$
3)  $1,728\ in^3$
4)  $1,230.9\ m^3$

5)  $1,017.9\ m^3$
6)  $217.7\ cm^3$
7)  $360\ yd^2$
8)  $864\ m^2$

9)  $64.34\ in^2$
10) $417.4\ cm^2$

# Chapter 13:

# Statistics and Probability

### Topics that you'll practice in this chapter:

✓ Mean and Median

✓ Mode and Range

✓ Pie Graph

✓ Probability Problems

✓ Factorials

✓ Combinations and Permutations

*Mathematics is no more computation than typing is literature.*

*– John Allen Paulos*

# *Mean and Median*

✑ *Find Mean and Median of the Given Data.*

1) $8, 12, 5, 3, 2$

2) $3, 6, 3, 7, 4, 13$

3) $13, 5, 1, 7, 9$

4) $6, 4, 2, 7, 3, 2$

5) $6, 5, 7, 5, 7, 1, 11$

6) $6, 1, 4, 4, 9, 2, 19$

7) $12, 4, 1, 5, 9, 7, 7, 19$

8) $18, 9, 5, 4, 9, 6, 12$

9) $28, 25, 15, 16, 32, 44, 71$

10) $10, 5, 1, 5, 4, 5, 8, 10$

11) $18, 15, 30, 64, 42, 11$

12) $44, 33, 56, 78, 41, 84$

✑ *Solve.*

13) In a javelin throw competition, five athletics score 56, 58, 63, 57 and 61 meters. What are their Mean and Median? _____

14) Eva went to shop and bought 3 apples, 5 peaches, 8 bananas, 1 pineapple and 3 melons. What are the Mean and Median of her purchase?

_____

15) Bob has 12 black pen, 14 red pen, 15 green pens, 24 blue pens and 3 boxes of yellow pens. If the Mean and Median are 16 and 15 respectively, what is the number of yellow pens in each box? _____

# Mode and Range

✍ *Find Mode and Rage of the Given Data.*

1) 8, 2, 5, 9, 1, 2

Mode: _____     Range: _____

2) 6, 6, 2, 3, 6, 3, 9, 12

Mode: _____     Range: _____

3) 4, 4, 3, 9, 7, 9, 4, 6, 4

Mode: _____     Range: _____

4) 12, 9, 2, 9, 3, 2, 9, 5

Mode: _____     Range: _____

5) 9, 5, 9, 5, 8, 9, 8

Mode: _____     Range: _____

6) 0, 1, 4, 10, 9, 2, 9, 1, 5, 1

Mode: _____     Range: _____

7) 6, 5, 6, 9, 7, 7, 5, 4, 3, 5

Mode: _____     Range: _____

8) 7, 5, 4, 9, 6, 7, 7, 5, 2

Mode: _____     Range: _____

9) 2, 2, 5, 6, 2, 4, 7, 6, 4, 9

Mode: _____     Range: _____

10) 7, 5, 2, 5, 4, 5, 8, 10

Mode: _____     Range: _____

11) 4, 1, 5, 2, 2, 12, 18, 2

Mode: _____     Range: _____

12) 6, 3, 5, 9, 6, 6, 3, 12

Mode: _____     Range: _____

✍ *Solve.*

13) A stationery sold 12 pencils, 36 red pens, 44 blue pens, 12 notebooks, 18 erasers, 34 rulers and 32 color pencils. What are the Mode and Range for the stationery sells?

Mode: _____     Range: _____

14) In an English test, eight students score 14, 13, 17, 11, 19, 20, 14 and 15. What are their Mode and Range? _____

15) What is the range of the first 6 even numbers greater than 11? _____

# *Pie Graph*

The circle graph below shows all Jason's expenses for last month. Jason spent $300 on his bills last month.

Answer following questions based on the Pie graph.

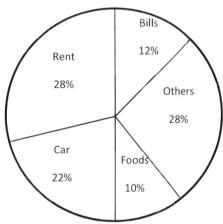

Jason's monthly expenses

1- How much did Jason spend on his car last month? _____

2- How much did Jason spend for foods last month? _____

3- How much did Jason spend on his rent last month? _____

4- What fraction is Jason's expenses for his bills and Car out of his total

   expenses last month? _____

5- How much was Jason's total expenses last month? _____

# *Probability Problems*

✍ *Solve.*

1) A number is chosen at random from 1 to 10. Find the probability of selecting number 4 or smaller numbers. _____

2) Bag A contains 9 red marbles and 3 green marbles. Bag B contains 9 black marbles and 6 orange marbles. What is the probability of selecting a green marble at random from bag A? What is the probability of selecting a black marble at random from Bag B? _____ _____

3) A number is chosen at random from 1 to 50. What is the probability of selecting multiples of 10. _____

4) A card is chosen from a well-shuffled deck of 52 cards. What is the probability that the card will be a king OR a queen? _____

5) A number is chosen at random from 1 to 10. What is the probability of selecting a multiple of 3. _____

A spinner, numbered 1–8, is spun once. What is the probability of spinning …

6) an EVEN number? _____    7) a multiple of 3? _____

8) a PRIME number? _____    9) number 9? _____

# *Factorials*

✎ *Determine the value for each expression.*

1) $3! + 2! =$

2) $3! + 6! =$

3) $(3!)^2 =$

4) $5! + 4! =$

5) $4! - 5! + 4 =$

6) $2! \times 5 - 12 =$

7) $(2! + 1!)^3 =$

8) $(3! + 0!)^3 =$

9) $(2! \cdot 0!)^4 - 1 =$

10) $\dfrac{7!}{4!} =$

11) $\dfrac{9!}{6!} =$

12) $\dfrac{8!}{5!} =$

13) $\dfrac{7!}{5!} =$

14) $\dfrac{20!}{18!} =$

15) $\dfrac{10!}{8!} =$

16) $\dfrac{(5+1!)^3}{3!} =$

17) $\dfrac{25!}{20!} =$

18) $\dfrac{22!}{18!5!} =$

19) $\dfrac{10!}{8!2!} =$

20) $\dfrac{100!}{97!} =$

21) $\dfrac{14!}{10!4!} =$

22) $\dfrac{14!}{9!3!} =$

23) $\dfrac{55!}{53!} =$

24) $\dfrac{(2 \cdot 3)!}{3!} =$

25) $\dfrac{4!(9n-1)!}{(9n)!} =$

26) $\dfrac{n(3n+8)!}{(3n+9)!} =$

27) $\dfrac{(n-2)!(n-1)}{(n+1)!} =$

# Combinations and Permutations

✍ *Calculate the value of each.*

1)  $4! = $ _____

2)  $4! \times 3! = $ _____

3)  $5! = $ _____

4)  $6! + 3! = $ _____

5)  $7! = $ _____

6)  $8! = $ _____

7)  $4! + 4! = $ _____

8)  $4! - 3! = $ _____

✍ *Solve each word problems.*

9)  Susan is baking cookies. She uses sugar, flour, butter, and eggs. How many different orders of ingredients can she try? _____

10) Jason is planning for his vacation. He wants to go to museum, watch a movie, go to the beach, and play volleyball. How many different ways of ordering are there for him? _____

11) How many 5-digit numbers can be named using the digits 1, 2, 3, 4, and 5 without repetition? _____

12) In how many ways can 5 boys be arranPSAT in a straight line? _____

13) In how many ways can 4 athletes be arranPSAT in a straight line? _____

14) A professor is going to arrange her 7 students in a straight line. In how many ways can she do this? _____

15) How many code symbols can be formed with the letters for the word WHITE? _____

16) In how many ways a team of 8 basketball players can to choose a captain and co-captain? _____

# *Answers of Worksheets – Chapter 13*

## Mean and Median

1) Mean: 6, Median: 5
2) Mean: 6, Median: 5
3) Mean: 7, Median: 7
4) Mean: 4, Median: 3.5
5) Mean: 6, Median: 6

6) Mean: 8, Median: 4
7) Mean: 8, Median: 7
8) Mean: 9, Median: 9
9) Mean: 33, Median: 28
10) Mean: 6, Median: 5

11) Mean: 30, Median: 24
12) Mean: 56, Median: 50
13) Mean: 59, Median: 58
14) Mean: 4, Median: 3
15) 5

## Mode and Range

1) Mode: 2, Range: 8
2) Mode: 6, Range: 10
3) Mode: 4, Range: 6
4) Mode: 9, Range: 10
5) Mode: 9, Range: 4

6) Mode: 1, Range: 10
7) Mode: 5, Range: 6
8) Mode: 7, Range: 7
9) Mode: 2, Range: 7
10) Mode: 5, Range: 8

11) Mode: 2, Range: 17
12) Mode: 6, Range: 9
13) Mode: 12, Range: 32
14) Mode: 14, Range: 9
15) 10

## Pie Graph

1) $550
2) $250
3) $700

4) $\frac{17}{50}$
5) $2,500

## Probability Problems

1) $\frac{2}{5}$
2) $\frac{1}{4}, \frac{3}{5}$
3) $\frac{1}{5}$

4) $\frac{2}{13}$
5) $\frac{3}{10}$
6) $\frac{1}{2}$

7) $\frac{1}{4}$
8) $\frac{1}{2}$
9) 0

## Factorials

1) 8
2) 726
3) 36
4) 144

5) −92
6) −2
7) 27
8) 125

9) 15
10) 210
11) 504
12) 336

13) 42

14) 380

15) 90

16) 36

17) 6,375,600

18) 1,463

19) 45

20) 970,200

21) 1,001

22) 40,040

23) 2,970

24) 120

25) $\frac{8}{3n}$

26) $\frac{n}{3(n+3)}$

27) $\frac{1}{n(n+1)}$

## Combinations and Permutations

1) 24

2) 144

3) 120

4) 726

5) 5,040

6) 40,320

7) 48

8) 18

9) 24

10) 24

11) 120

12) 120

13) 24

14) 5,040

15) 120

16) 56

# Chapter 14:

# Complex Numbers

**Topics that you'll practice in this chapter:**

- ✓ Adding and Subtracting Complex Numbers

- ✓ Multiplying and Dividing Complex Numbers

- ✓ Graphing Complex Numbers

- ✓ Rationalizing Imaginary Denominators

*Mathematics is a hard thing to love. It has the unfortunate habit, like a rude dog, of turning its most unfavorable side towards you when you first make contact with it. — David Whiteland*

# Adding and Subtracting Complex Numbers

✍ *Simplify.*

1) $(2i) - (i) =$

2) $(2i) + (2i) =$

3) $(i) + (3i) =$

4) $(-2i) - (6i) =$

5) $(5i) + (4i) =$

6) $(3i) - (-7i) =$

7) $(-6i) + (-9i) =$

8) $(15i) - (7i) =$

9) $(-12i) - (5i) =$

10) $(2i) + (2 + 3i) =$

11) $(2 - 4i) + (-i) =$

12) $(-3i) + (3 + 5i) =$

13) $3 + (2 - 4i) =$

14) $(-5i) - (-5 + 2i) =$

15) $(5 + 3i) - (-4i) =$

16) $(8 + 5i) + (-7i) =$

17) $(9i) - (-6i + 10) =$

18) $(12i + 8) + (-7i) =$

19) $(13i) - (17 + 3i) =$

20) $(3 + 5i) + (8 + 3i) =$

21) $(8 - 3i) + (4 + i) =$

22) $(10 + 9i) + (6 + 8i) =$

23) $(-3 + 6i) - (-9 - i) =$

24) $(-5 + 15i) - (-3 + 3i) =$

25) $(-14 + i) - (-12 - 11i) =$

26) $(-18 - 3i) + (11 + 5i) =$

27) $(-11 - 9i) - (-9 - 3i) =$

28) $-8 + (2i) + (-8 + 6i) =$

29) $12 - (5i) + (4 - 14i) =$

30) $-2 + (-8 - 7i) - 9 =$

31) $(-12i) + (2 - 6i) + 10 =$

32) $(-8i) - (8 - 5i) + 6i =$

# *Multiplying and Dividing Complex Numbers*

✍ *Simplify.*

1) $(5i)(-i) =$

2) $(-4i)(5i) =$

3) $(i)(7i)(-i) =$

4) $(3i)(-4i) =$

5) $(-2-i)(4+i) =$

6) $(2-2i)^2 =$

7) $(4-3i)(6-6i) =$

8) $(5+4i)^2 =$

9) $(4i)(-i)(2-5i) =$

10) $(2-8i)(3-5i) =$

11) $(-5+9i)(3+5i) =$

12) $(7+3i)(7+8i) =$

13) $2(3i) - (5i)(-8+5i) =$

14) $\dfrac{5}{-10i} =$

15) $\dfrac{4-3i}{-4i} =$

16) $\dfrac{5+9i}{i} =$

17) $\dfrac{12}{-9+3i} =$

18) $\dfrac{-3-10}{5i} =$

19) $\dfrac{9i}{3-i} =$

20) $\dfrac{2+4i}{14+4i} =$

21) $\dfrac{5+6i}{-1+8i} =$

22) $\dfrac{-8-i}{-4-6i} =$

23) $\dfrac{-1+5i}{-8-7i} =$

24) $\dfrac{-2-9i}{-2+7i} =$

25) $\dfrac{4+i}{2-5i} =$

# *Graphing Complex Numbers*

✎ *Identify each complex number graphed.*

1)

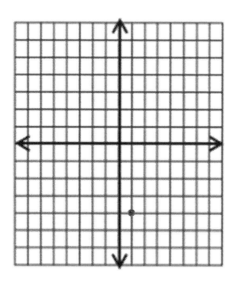

2)

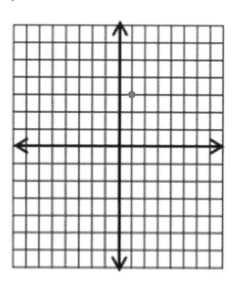

3)

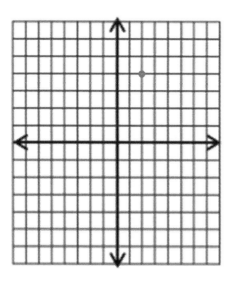

4)

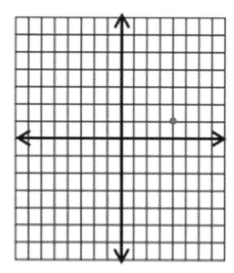

# *Rationalizing Imaginary Denominators*

✎ **Simplify.**

1) $\dfrac{-2}{-2i} =$

2) $\dfrac{-1}{-9i} =$

3) $\dfrac{-8}{-5i} =$

4) $\dfrac{-5}{-i} =$

5) $\dfrac{3}{5i} =$

6) $\dfrac{6}{-4i} =$

7) $\dfrac{6}{-7i} =$

8) $\dfrac{-10}{3i} =$

9) $\dfrac{a}{bi} =$

10) $\dfrac{10-10}{-5i} =$

11) $\dfrac{4-9i}{-6i} =$

12) $\dfrac{6+8i}{9i} =$

13) $\dfrac{8i}{-1+3i} =$

14) $\dfrac{5i}{-2-6i} =$

15) $\dfrac{-10-5i}{-6+6i} =$

16) $\dfrac{-5-9i}{9+8i} =$

17) $\dfrac{-5-3i}{7-10i} =$

18) $\dfrac{-1+i}{-5i} =$

19) $\dfrac{-6-i}{i} =$

20) $\dfrac{-4-i}{9+5i} =$

21) $\dfrac{-3+i}{-2i} =$

22) $\dfrac{-6-i}{-1+6i} =$

23) $\dfrac{-9-3i}{-3+3i} =$

24) $\dfrac{4i+1}{-1+3i} =$

# *Answers of Worksheets – Chapter 14*

### *Adding and Subtracting Complex Numbers*

1) $i$
2) $4i$
3) $4i$
4) $-8i$
5) $9i$
6) $10i$
7) $-15i$
8) $8i$
9) $-17i$
10) $2 + 5i$
11) $2 - 5i$

12) $3 + 2i$
13) $5 - 4i$
14) $5 - 7i$
15) $5 + 7i$
16) $8 - 2i$
17) $10 + 15i$
18) $8 + 5i$
19) $-17 + 10i$
20) $11 + 8i$
21) $12 - 2i$
22) $16 + 17i$

23) $6 + 7i$
24) $-2 + 12i$
25) $-2 + 12i$
26) $-7 + 2i$
27) $-2 - 6i$
28) $-16 + 8i$
29) $16 - 19i$
30) $-19 - 7i$
31) $12 - 18i$
32) $-8 + 3i$

### *Multiplying and Dividing Complex Numbers*

1) $5$
2) $20$
3) $7i$
4) $12$
5) $-7 - 6i$
6) $-8i$
7) $6 - 42i$
8) $9 + 40i$
9) $8 - 20i$
10) $-34 - 34i$
11) $-60 + 2i$

12) $25 + 77i$
13) $25 + 46i$
14) $\dfrac{i}{2}$
15) $\dfrac{3}{4} + i$
16) $9 - 5i$
17) $\dfrac{2}{5} - \dfrac{6}{5}i$
18) $-2 + \dfrac{3}{5}i$
19) $-\dfrac{9}{10} + \dfrac{27}{10}i$

20) $\dfrac{11}{53} + \dfrac{12}{53}i$
21) $\dfrac{43}{65} - \dfrac{46}{65}i$
22) $\dfrac{19}{26} + \dfrac{11}{13}i$
23) $-\dfrac{27}{113} - \dfrac{47}{113}i$
24) $-\dfrac{59}{53} + \dfrac{32}{53}i$
25) $\dfrac{3}{29} + \dfrac{22}{29}i$

### *Graphing Complex Numbers*

1) $1 - 4i$
2) $1 + 3i$

3) $2 + 4i$
4) $4 + i$

### *Rationalizing Imaginary Denominators*

1) $-i$
2) $-\dfrac{1}{9}i$
3) $\dfrac{-8}{5}i$
4) $-5i$

5) $-\dfrac{3}{5}i$
6) $\dfrac{3}{2}i$
7) $\dfrac{6}{7}i$

8) $\dfrac{10}{3}i$
9) $-\dfrac{a}{b}i$
10) $2 + 2i$

11) $\frac{2}{3} + \frac{3}{2}i$

12) $\frac{6}{91} + \frac{8}{91}i$

13) $\frac{12}{5} - \frac{4}{5}i$

14) $-\frac{3}{4} - \frac{1}{4}i$

15) $\frac{5}{12} + \frac{5}{4}i$

16) $-\frac{117}{145} - \frac{41}{145}i$

17) $-\frac{5}{149} - \frac{71}{149}i$

18) $-\frac{1}{5} - \frac{1}{5}i$

19) $-1 + 6i$

20) $-\frac{41}{106} + \frac{11}{106}i$

21) $-\frac{1}{2} - \frac{3}{2}i$

22) $i$

23) $1 + 2i$

24) $\frac{11}{10} - \frac{7}{10}i$

# Chapter 15:

# Logarithms

**Topics that you'll practice in this chapter:**

- ✓ Rewriting Logarithms
- ✓ Evaluating Logarithms
- ✓ Properties of Logarithms
- ✓ Natural Logarithms
- ✓ Exponential Equations Requiring Logarithms
- ✓ Solving Logarithmic Equations

*Mathematics is an art of human understanding. — William Thurston*

# *Rewriting Logarithms*

 **Rewrite each equation in exponential form.**

1) $log_5 25 = 2$

2) $log_4 256 = 4$

3) $log_6 36 = 2$

4) $log_5 125 = 3$

5) $log_7 49 = 2$

6) $log_6 216 = 3$

7) $log_2 16 = 4$

8) $log_3 81 = 4$

9) $log_{10} 100 = 2$

10) $log_7 343 = 3$

11) $log_4 64 = 3$

12) $log_9 81 = 2$

13) $log_5 625 = 4$

14) $log_9 3 = \frac{1}{2}$

15) $log_{64} 8 = \frac{1}{2}$

16) $log_{125} 5 = \frac{1}{3}$

17) $log_{16} 2 = \frac{1}{4}$

18) $log_8 \frac{1}{64} = -2$

19) $log_5 \frac{1}{125} = -3$

20) $log_a \frac{5}{8} = b$

 **Rewrite each exponential equation in logarithmic form.**

21) $3^4 = 81$

22) $5^2 = 25$

23) $2^5 = 32$

24) $6^3 = 216$

25) $7^2 = 49$

26) $8^3 = 512$

27) $5^3 = 125$

28) $2^8 = 256$

29) $2^{-3} = \frac{1}{8}$

30) $3^{-4} = \frac{1}{81}$

31) $5^{-2} = \frac{1}{25}$

32) $6^{-3} = \frac{1}{216}$

33) $4^{-3} = \frac{1}{64}$

34) $2^{-6} = \frac{1}{64}$

# *Evaluating Logarithms*

✎ **Evaluate each logarithm.**

1) $\log_2 4 =$

2) $\log_2 8 =$

3) $\log_3 27 =$

4) $\log_3 9 =$

5) $\log_4 16 =$

6) $\log_2 32 =$

7) $\log_8 64 =$

8) $\log_2 \frac{1}{2} =$

9) $\log_2 \frac{1}{8} =$

10) $\log_3 \frac{1}{3} =$

11) $\log_4 \frac{1}{16} =$

12) $\log_3 \frac{1}{9} =$

13) $\log_7 \frac{1}{49} =$

14) $\log_{64} \frac{1}{4} =$

15) $\log_{625} 5 =$

16) $\log_2 \frac{1}{64} =$

17) $\log_4 \frac{1}{64} =$

18) $\log_{36} \frac{1}{6} =$

✎ **Circle the points which are on the graph of the given logarithmic functions.**

19) $y = 2\log_3(x + 1) + 2$  (2, 4),  (8, 4),  (0, 3)

20) $y = 3\log_3(3x) - 2$  (3, 6),  (3, 4),  $(\frac{1}{3}, 2)$

21) $y = -2\log_2 2(x - 1) + 1$  (3, −3),  (2, 1),  (5, 5)

22) $y = 4\log_4(4x) + 7$  (1, 7),  (1, 11),  (4, 8)

23) $y = -\log_2 2(x + 3) + 1$  (−2, 0),  (1, 2),  (5, 3)

24) $y = -\log_5(x - 3) + 8$  (4, 8),  (8, 8),  (4, 4)

25) $y = 3\log_4(x + 1) + 3$  (3, 3),  (3, 6),  (0, 4)

# *Properties of Logarithms*

✎ **Expand each logarithm.**

1) $\log (8 \times 5) =$

2) $\log (9 \times 4) =$

3) $\log (3 \times 7) =$

4) $\log \left(\frac{3}{4}\right) =$

5) $\log \left(\frac{5}{7}\right) =$

6) $\log \left(\frac{2}{5}\right)^3 =$

7) $\log (2 \times 3^4) =$

8) $\log \left(\frac{5}{7}\right)^4 =$

9) $\log \left(\frac{2^3}{7}\right) =$

10) $\log (x \times y)^5 =$

11) $\log (x^3 \times y \times z^4) =$

12) $\log \left(\frac{u^4}{v}\right) =$

13) $\log \left(\frac{x}{y^6}\right) =$

✎ **Condense each expression to a single logarithm.**

14) $\log 2 - \log 9 =$

15) $\log 5 + \log 3 =$

16) $5 \log 6 - 3 \log 4 =$

17) $4 \log 7 - 2 \log 9 =$

18) $3 \log 5 - \log 14 =$

19) $7 \log 3 - 4\log 4 =$

20) $\log 7 - 2 \log 12 =$

21) $2\log 5 + 3\log 8 =$

22) $4\log 3 + 5\log 7 =$

23) $4 \log_5 a + 7 \log_5 b =$

24) $2\log_3 x - 9 \log_3 y =$

25) $\log_4 u - 6 \log_4 v =$

26) $4 \log_6 u + 8 \log_6 v =$

27) $4 \log_3 u - 20 \log_3 v =$

# Natural Logarithms

✍ **Solve each equation for** x.

1) $e^x = 3$

2) $e^x = 4$

3) $e^x = 8$

4) $ln\ x = 6$

5) $ln\ (ln\ x) = 5$

6) $e^x = 9$

7) $ln(2x + 5) = 4$

8) $ln(2x - 1) = 1$

9) $ln(6x - 1) = 1$

10) $ln\ x = \frac{1}{2}$

11) $ln2x = e^2$

12) $ln\ x = ln\ 4 + ln\ 7$

13) $ln\ x = 2ln\ 4 + ln\ 5$

✍ **Evaluate without using a calculator.**

14) $ln\ 1 =$

15) $ln\ e^3 =$

16) $2\ln e =$

17) $ln\ e^2 =$

18) $4ln\ e =$

19) $ln\left(\frac{1}{e}\right) =$

20) $e^{ln10} =$

21) $e^{3ln2} =$

22) $e^{5ln2} =$

23) $ln\ \sqrt{e} =$

✍ **Reduce the following expressions to simplest form.**

24) $e^{-2ln5+2ln3} =$

25) $e^{-ln\left(\frac{1}{e}\right)} =$

26) $2\ ln(e^3) =$

27) $ln(\frac{1}{e})^2 =$

28) $e^{ln2+3ln2} =$

29) $e^{ln\left(\frac{2}{e}\right)} =$

30) $5\ ln(1^{-e}) =$

31) $ln(\frac{1}{e})^{-3} =$

32) $ln(\frac{\sqrt{e}}{e}) =$

33) $e^{-2lne+2ln} =$

34) $e^{ln\frac{1}{e}} =$

35) $3\ ln(e^e) =$

# *Exponential Equations and Logarithms*

 **Solve each equation for the unknown variable.**

1) $5^{3n} = 125$

2) $3^r = 69$

3) $20^n = 56$

4) $4^{r+1} = 1$

5) $243^x = 81$

6) $6^{-3v-2} = 36$

7) $3^{2n} = 9$

8) $6^n = 51$

9) $\frac{216^{2a}}{36^{-a}} = 216$

10) $25 \times 25^{-v} = 625$

11) $3^{2n} = \frac{1}{81}$

12) $(\frac{1}{6})^n = 36$

13) $32^{2x} = 8$

14) $5^{3-2x} = 5^{-x}$

15) $2^{-3x} = 2^{x-1}$

16) $2^{2n} = 16$

17) $2^{2x+2} = 2^{3x}$

18) $5^{3n} = 125$

19) $3^{-2k} = 81$

20) $5^{3r} = 5^{-2r}$

21) $4^{-2r} \times 4^r = 64$

22) $10^{3x} = 10{,}000$

23) $25 \cdot 125^{-v} = 625$

24) $\frac{125}{25^{-3m}} = 25^{-2m-2}$

25) $2^{-2n} \times 2^{n+1} = 2^{-2n}$

26) $6^{3n} \times 6^{-n} = 6^{-2n}$

 **Solve each problem. (Round to the nearest whole number)**

27) A substance decays 18% each day. After 12 days, there are 6 milligrams of the substance remaining. How many milligrams were there initially? _____

28) A culture of bacteria grows continuously. The culture doubles every 3 hours. If the initial amount of bacteria is 10, how many bacteria will there be in 13 hours? _____

29) Bob plans to invest $5,500 at an annual rate of 4.5%. How much will Bob have in the account after five years if the balance is compounded quarterly? _____

30) Suppose you plan to invest $4,000 at an annual rate of 5.5%. How much will you have in the account after 10 years if the balance is compounded monthly? _____

# *Solving Logarithmic Equations*

 **Find the value of the variables in each equation.**

1) $2\log_7 - 2x = 0$

2) $-\log_5 7x = 2$

3) $\log x + 5 = 2$

4) $\log x - \log 4 = 3$

5) $\log x + \log 2 = 4$

6) $\log 10 + \log x = 1$

7) $\log x + \log 8 = \log 48$

*8) $-3\log_3(x - 2) = -12$

9) $\log 6x = \log(x + 5)$

10) $\log(4k - 5) = \log(2k - 1)$

11) $\log(4p - 2) = \log(-5p + 5)$

12) $-10 + \log_3(n + 3) = -10$

13) $\log_9(x + 2) = \log_9(x^2 + 30)$

14) $\log_{12}(v^2 + 35) = \log_{12}(-2v - 1)$

15) $\log(16 + 2b) = \log(b^2 - 4b)$

16) $\log_9(x + 6) - \log_9 x = \log_9 2$

17) $\log_5 6 + \log_5 2x^2 = \log_5 48$

18) $\log_6(x + 1) - \log_6 x = \log_6 29$

 **Find the value of** x **in each natural logarithm equation.**

19) $\ln 2 - \ln(3x + 2) = 1$

20) $\ln(x - 3) - \ln(x - 5) = \ln 5$

21) $\ln e^4 - \ln(x + 1) = 1$

22) $\ln(2x - 1) - \ln(x - 5) = \ln 5$

23) $\ln 2x + \ln(3x - 4) = \ln 4x$

24) $\ln(4x - 2) - 4\ln(x - 5) = \ln 10$

25) $\ln(4x + 2) - \ln 1 = 5$

26) $\ln(x - 3) + \ln(x - 5) = \ln 2$

27) $\ln 2 + \ln(3x + 2) = 4$

28) $2\ln 4x - \ln(x + 6) = 2\ln 3x$

29) $\ln x^2 + \ln x^3 = \ln 1$

30) $\ln x^4 - \ln(x + 4) = 4\ln x$

31) $2\ln(x - 3) = \ln(x^2 - 6x + 9)$

32) $\ln(x^2 + 12) = \ln(6x + 4)$

33) $2\ln x - 2\ln(x + 2) = 4\ln(x^2)$

34) $\ln(4x - 3) - \ln(2x - 4) = \ln 5$

35) $\ln 2 + 4\ln(x + 2) = \ln 2$

36) $2\ln e^2 + \ln(2x - 1) = \ln 5 + 4$

# *Answers of Worksheets – Chapter 15*

## *Rewriting Logarithms*

1) $5^2 = 25$
2) $4^4 = 256$
3) $6^2 = 36$
4) $5^3 = 125$
5) $7^2 = 49$
6) $6^3 = 216$
7) $2^4 = 16$
8) $3^4 = 81$
9) $10^2 = 100$
10) $7^3 = 343$
11) $4^3 = 64$
12) $9^2 = 81$
13) $5^4 = 625$
14) $9^{\frac{1}{2}} = 3$
15) $64^{\frac{1}{2}} = 8$
16) $125^{\frac{1}{3}} = 5$

17) $16^{\frac{1}{4}} = 2$
18) $8^{-2} = \frac{1}{64}$
19) $5^{-3} = \frac{1}{125}$
20) $a^b = \frac{5}{8}$
21) $log_3 81 = 4$
22) $log_5 25 = 2$
23) $log_2 32 = 5$
24) $log_6 216 = 3$
25) $log_7 49 = 2$
26) $log_8 512 = 3$
27) $log_5 125 = 3$

28) $log_2 256 = 8$
29) $log_2 \frac{1}{8} = -3$
30) $log_3 \frac{1}{81} = -4$
31) $log_5 \frac{1}{25} = -2$
32) $log_6 \frac{1}{216} = -3$
33) $log_4 \frac{1}{64} = -3$
34) $log_2 \frac{1}{64} = -6$

## *Evaluating Logarithms*

1) 2
2) 3
3) 3
4) 2
5) 2
6) 5
7) 2
8) $-1$
9) $-3$

10) $-1$
11) $-2$
12) $-2$
13) $-2$
14) $-\frac{1}{3}$
15) $-4$
16) $-6$
17) $-3$

18) $-\frac{1}{2}$
19) $(2,4)$
20) $(3,4)$
21) $(3,-3)$
22) $(1,11)$
23) $(-2,1)$
24) $(4,8)$
25) $(3,6)$

## *Properties of Logarithms*

1) $log\ 8 + log\ 5$
2) $log\ 9 + log\ 9$
3) $log\ 3 + log\ 7$
4) $log\ 3 - log\ 4$
5) $log\ 5 - log\ 7$

6) $3\ log\ 2 - 3\ log\ 5$
7) $log\ 2 + 4\ log\ 3$
8) $4log\ 5 - 4\ log\ 7$
9) $3\ log\ 2 - log\ 7$
10) $5\ log\ x + 5\ log\ y$

11) $log\ x + log\ y + 4\ log\ z$

12) $4\ log\ u - log\ v$

13) $log\ x - 6\ log\ y$

14) $log\ \frac{2}{9}$

15) $log(5 \cdot 3)$

16) $log\ \frac{6^5}{4^3}$

17) $log\ \frac{7^4}{9^2}$

18) $log\ \frac{5^3}{14}$

19) $log\ \frac{3^7}{4^4}$

20) $log\ \frac{7}{12^2}$

21) $log\ (5^2 8^3)$

22) $log\ (3^4 7^5)$

23) $log_5\ (a^4 b^7)$

24) $log_3\ \frac{x^2}{y^9}$

25) $log_4\ \frac{u}{v^6}$

26) $log_6(u^4 \times v^8)$

27) $log_3\ \frac{u^4}{v^{20}}$

## Natural Logarithms

1) $x = ln\ 3$

2) $x = ln\ 4, x = 2ln(2)$

3) $x = ln\ 8, x = 3ln(2)$

4) $x = e^6$

5) $x = e^{e^5}$

6) $x = ln\ 9, x = 2ln(3)$

7) $x = \frac{e^4 - 5}{2}$

8) $x = \frac{e+1}{2}$

9) $x = \frac{e+1}{6}$

10) $x = \sqrt{e}$

11) $x = \frac{e e^2}{2}$

12) $x = 28$

13) $x = 80$

14) $0$

15) $3$

16) $2$

17) $2$

18) $4$

19) $-1$

20) $10$

21) $8$

22) $32$

23) $\frac{1}{2}$

24) $\frac{9}{25} = 0.36$

25) $e$

26) $6$

27) $-2$

28) $16$

29) $\frac{2}{e}$

30) $0$

31) $3$

32) $-0.5$

33) $4e^{-2} = \frac{4}{e^2}$

34) $\frac{1}{e}$

35) $3e$

## Exponential Equations and Logarithms

1) $1$

2) $3.854$

3) $1.3437$

4) $-1$

5) $\frac{4}{5}$

6) $-\frac{4}{3}$

7) $1$

8) $51$

9) $\frac{3}{8}$

10) $-1$

11) $-2$

12) $-2$

13) $\frac{3}{10}$

14) $3$

15) $\frac{1}{4}$

16) $2$

17) $2$

18) $1$

19) $-2$

20) $0$

21) $-3$

22) $\frac{4}{3}$

23) $-1$

24) $-\frac{7}{10}$

25) $-1$

26) $0$

27) $52$

28) 202                              29) $6879.13                         30) $6,924.31

## *Solving Logarithmic Equations*

1) $\{-\frac{1}{2}\}$

2) $\{\frac{1}{175}\}$

3) $\{-\frac{1}{1,000}\}$

4) $\{4,000\}$

5) $\{5,000\}$

6) $\{1\}$

7) $\{6\}$

8) $\{83\}$

9) $\{1\}$

10) $\{2\}$

11) $\{\frac{7}{9}\}$

12) $\{-2\}$

13) No Solution

14) No Solution

15) $\{8, -2\}$

16) $\{6\}$

17) $\{\sqrt{3}, -\sqrt{3}\}$

18) $\{\frac{1}{28}\}$

19) $x = \frac{2-2e}{3e} = -0.42$

20) $\{\frac{11}{2}\}$

21) $e^3 - 1$

22) $\{8\}$

23) $\{2\}$

24) $\{6.23\}$

25) $x = \frac{e^5-2}{4}$

26) $x = 4 + \sqrt{3}$

27) $x = \frac{e^4-4}{6}$

28) No Solution

29) $\{1\}$

30) No Solution

31) $x > 3$

32) $\{2, 4\}$

33) $\{0.71667 \dots\}$

34) $\{\frac{17}{6}\}$

35) $\{-1\}$

36) $\{3\}$

# Chapter 16:

# Trigonometric Functions

## Topics that you'll practice in this chapter:

- ✓ Trig ratios of General Angles
- ✓ Sketch Each Angle in Standard Position
- ✓ Finding Co–Terminal Angles and Reference Angles
- ✓ Angles in Radians
- ✓ Angles in Degrees
- ✓ Evaluating Each Trigonometric Expression
- ✓ Missing Sides and Angles of a Right Triangle
- ✓ Arc Length and Sector Area

*Mathematics is like checkers in being suitable for the young, not too difficult, amusing, and*

*without peril to the state. — Plato*

# Trig ratios of General Angles

✍ *Evaluate.*

1) $\sin -60° =$ _____

2) $\sin 150° =$ _____

3) $\cos 315° =$ _____

4) $\cos 180° =$ _____

5) $\sin 120° =$ _____

6) $\sin -330° =$ _____

7) $\tan -90° =$ _____

8) $\cot 90° =$ _____

9) $\tan 270° =$ _____

10) $\cot 150° =$ _____

11) $\sec 120° =$ _____

12) $\csc -360° =$ _____

13) $\cot -270° =$ _____

14) $\sec 90° =$ _____

15) $\cos -90° =$ _____

16) $\sec 60° =$ _____

17) $\csc 480° =$ _____

18) $\cot -135° =$ _____

✍ *Find the exact value of each trigonometric function. Some may be undefined.*

19) $\sec \pi =$ _____

20) $\tan -\frac{3\pi}{2} =$ _____

21) $\cos \frac{11\pi}{6} =$ _____

22) $\cot \frac{5\pi}{3} =$ _____

23) $\sec -\frac{3\pi}{4} =$ _____

24) $\sec \frac{\pi}{3} =$ _____

25) $\csc \frac{5\pi}{6} =$ _____

26) $\cot \frac{4\pi}{3} =$ _____

27) $\csc -\frac{3\pi}{4} =$ _____

28) $\cot \frac{2\pi}{3} =$ _____

# Sketch Each Angle in Standard Position

 *Draw each angle with the given measure in standard position.*

1) $-120°$

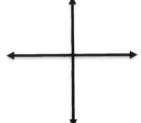

4) $280°$

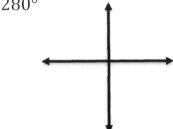

2) $440°$

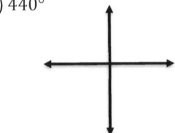

5) $710°$

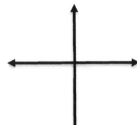

3) $-\frac{10\pi}{3}$

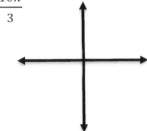

6) $\frac{11\pi}{6}$

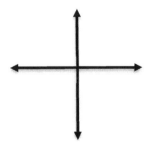

# Finding Co-terminal Angles and Reference Angles

 *Find a conterminal angle between 0° and 360° for each angle provided.*

1) $-440° =$

3) $-435° =$

2) $640° =$

4) $-330° =$

 *Find a conterminal angle between 0 and 2π for each given angle.*

5) $\dfrac{15\pi}{4} =$

7) $-\dfrac{35\pi}{18} =$

6) $-\dfrac{19\pi}{12} =$

8) $\dfrac{11\pi}{3} =$

 *Find the reference angle of each angle.*

9)

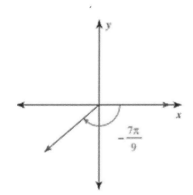

10)

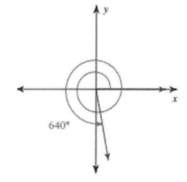

# *Angles and Angle Measure*

 **Convert each degree measure into radians.**

1) $-140° =$ ____

2) $320° =$ ____

3) $210° =$ ____

4) $780° =$ ____

5) $-190° =$ ____

6) $345° =$ ____

7) $-150° =$ ____

8) $420° =$ ____

9) $300° =$ ____

10) $-60° =$ ____

11) $315° =$ ____

12) $600° =$ ____

13) $-720° =$ ____

14) $-160° =$ ____

15) $-210° =$ ____

16) $960° =$ ____

17) $-30° =$ ____

18) $660° =$ ____

19) $-240° =$ ____

20) $840° =$ ____

21) $1,200° =$ ____

 **Convert each radian measure into degrees.**

22) $\dfrac{\pi}{30} =$

23) $\dfrac{4\pi}{5} =$

24) $\dfrac{7\pi}{18} =$

25) $\dfrac{\pi}{5} =$

26) $-\dfrac{5\pi}{4} =$

27) $\dfrac{14\pi}{3} =$

28) $-\dfrac{16\pi}{3} =$

29) $-\dfrac{3\pi}{5} =$

30) $\dfrac{11}{6} =$

31) $\dfrac{5\pi}{9} =$

32) $-\dfrac{\pi}{3} =$

33) $\dfrac{13\pi}{6} =$

34) $\dfrac{9\pi}{4} =$

35) $\dfrac{21\pi}{4} =$

36) $-\dfrac{4\pi}{15} =$

37) $\dfrac{14}{3} =$

38) $-\dfrac{41\pi}{12} =$

39) $-\dfrac{17}{9} =$

# Evaluating Trigonometric Functions

✎ *Find the exact value of each trigonometric function.*

1) $\cos 225° =$ _____

2) $\tan \dfrac{7\pi}{6} =$

3) $\tan -\dfrac{\pi}{6} =$ _____

4) $\cot -\dfrac{7\pi}{6} =$ _____

5) $\cos -\dfrac{\pi}{4} =$ _____

6) $\cos -480° =$ _____

7) $\sin 690° =$ _____

8) $\tan 420° =$ _____

9) $\cot -495° =$ _____

10) $\tan 405° =$ _____

11) $\cot 390° =$ _____

12) $\cos -300° =$ _____

13) $\cot -210° =$ _____

✎ *Use the given point on the terminal side of angle $\theta$ to find the value of the trigonometric function indicated.*

14) $\sin\theta; \ (-6, 4)$

15) $\cos\theta; \ (2, -2)$

16) $\cot\theta; \ (-7, \sqrt{15})$

17) $\cos\theta; \ (-5, -12)$

18) $\sin\theta; \ (-\sqrt{7}, 3)$

19) $\tan\theta; \ (-11, -2)$

# *Missing Sides and Angles of a Right Triangle*

 *Find the value of each trigonometric ratio as fractions in their simplest form.*

1) $tan\ A$

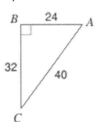

2) $sin\ x$

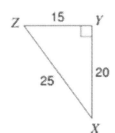

 *Find the missing sides. Round answers to the nearest tenth.*

3)

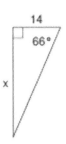

4)

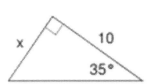

5)

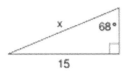

6)

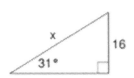

# *Arc Length and Sector Area*

🖎 *Find the length of each arc. Round your answers to the nearest tenth.*

$(\pi = 3.14)$

1) $r = 28$ cm, $\theta = 45\circ$

2) $r = 15$ ft, $\theta = 95\circ$

3) $r = 22$ ft, $\theta = 60\circ$

4) $r = 12\ m,\ \theta = 85\circ$

🖎 *Find area of each sector. Do not round. Round your answers to the nearest tenth.* $(\pi = 3.14)$

5)

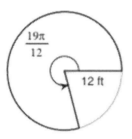

7)

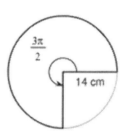

6)

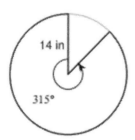

8)

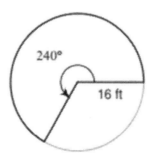

# *Answers of Worksheets – Chapter 16*

## *Trig Ratios of General Angles*

1) $-\frac{\sqrt{3}}{2}$

2) $\frac{1}{2}$

3) $\frac{\sqrt{2}}{2}$

4) $-1$

5) $\frac{\sqrt{3}}{2}$

6) $\frac{1}{2}$

7) Undefined

8) $0$

9) Undefined

10) $-\sqrt{3}$

11) $-2$

12) $1$

13) $0$

14) Undefined

15) $0$

16) $2$

17) $\frac{2\sqrt{3}}{3}$

18) $1$

19) $-1$

20) Undefined

21) $\frac{\sqrt{3}}{2}$

22) $-\frac{\sqrt{3}}{3}$

23) $-\sqrt{2}$

24) $2$

25) $2$

26) $\frac{\sqrt{3}}{3}$

27) $-\sqrt{2}$

28) $-\frac{\sqrt{3}}{3}$

## *Sketch Each Angle in Standard Position*

1) $-120°$
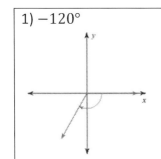

2) $440°$

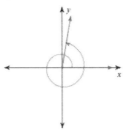

3) $-\frac{10\pi}{3}$
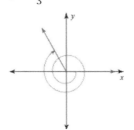

4) $280°$
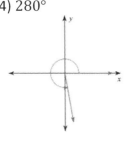

5) $710°$
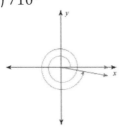

6) $\frac{11\pi}{6}$
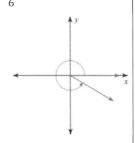

## *Finding Co–Terminal Angles and Reference Angles*

1)  $280°$

2)  $280°$

3)  $285°$

4) $30°$

5) $\frac{7\pi}{4}$

6) $\frac{5\pi}{12}$

7) $\frac{\pi}{18}$

8) $\frac{5\pi}{3}$

9) $\frac{2\pi}{9}$

10) $80°$

## Angles and Angle Measure

1) $-\frac{7\pi}{9}$

2) $\frac{16\pi}{9}$

3) $\frac{7\pi}{6}$

4) $\frac{13}{3}$

5) $-\frac{19\pi}{18}$

6) $\frac{23}{12}$

7) $-\frac{5\pi}{6}$

8) $\frac{7\pi}{3}$

9) $\frac{5\pi}{3}$

10) $-\frac{\pi}{3}$

11) $\frac{7\pi}{4}$

12) $\frac{10\pi}{3}$

13) $-4\pi$

14) $-\frac{8\pi}{9}$

15) $-\frac{7\pi}{6}$

16) $\frac{16\pi}{3}$

17) $-\frac{\pi}{6}$

18) $\frac{11\pi}{3}$

19) $-\frac{4\pi}{3}$

20) $\frac{14}{3}$

21) $\frac{20}{3}$

22) $6°$

23) $144°$

24) $70°$

25) $36°$

26) $-225°$

27) $840°$

28) $-960°$

29) $-108°$

30) $330°$

31) $100°$

32) $-60°$

33) $390°$

34) $405°$

35) $945°$

36) $-48°$

37) $840°$

38) $-615°$

39) $-340°$

## Evaluating Each Trigonometric Expression

1) $-\frac{\sqrt{2}}{2}$

2) $\frac{\sqrt{3}}{3}$

3) $-\frac{\sqrt{3}}{3}$

4) $-\sqrt{3}$

5) $\frac{\sqrt{2}}{2}$

6) $-\frac{1}{2}$

7) $-\frac{1}{2}$

8) $\sqrt{3}$

9) $1$

10) $1$

11) $\sqrt{3}$

12) $\frac{1}{2}$

13) $-\sqrt{3}$

14) $\frac{2\sqrt{13}}{13}$

15) $\sqrt{2}$

16) $-\dfrac{7\sqrt{15}}{15}$

17) $-\dfrac{5}{13}$

18) $\dfrac{3}{4}$

19) $\dfrac{2}{11}$

## Missing Sides and Angles of a Right Triangle

1) $\dfrac{4}{3}$

2) $\dfrac{3}{5}$

3) 31.4

4) 7.0

5) 16.2

6) 31.1

## Arc Length and Sector Area

1) $22\ cm$

2) $24.9\ ft$

3) $23\ ft$

4) $17.8\ m$

5) $358\ ft^2$

6) $538.5\ in^2$

7) $461.6\ cm^2$

8) $535.9\ ft^2$

# PSAT Math Practice Tests

The Preliminary SAT/ National Merit Scholarship Qualifying Test (PSAT/NMSQT) is a standardized test used for college admissions in the United States. 10th and 11th graders take the PSAT to practice for the SAT and to secure a National Merit distinction or scholarship.

The PSAT is similar to the SAT in both format and content. There are three sections on the PSAT:

- Reading
- Math
- Writing

The PSAT Math section is divided into two subsections:

A **No Calculator Section** contains 17 questions and students cannot use a calculator. Students have 25 minutes to complete this section.

A **Calculator Section** contains 31 questions. Students have 45 minutes to complete this section.

40 questions are multiple choice questions and 8 questions are grid-ins.

PSAT Math cover the following topics:

- Pre-Algebra
- Algebra
- Coordinate Geometry
- Plane Geometry
- Date analysis and basic Statistics
- Trigonometry

In this section, there are two complete PSAT Math Tests. Take these tests to see what score you'll be able to receive on a real PSAT test.

Good luck!

# Time to Test

## Time to refine your skill with a practice examination

Take practice PSAT Math Tests to simulate the test day experience. After you've finished, score your tests using the answer keys.

## Before You Start

- You'll need a pencil, a timer and a calculator to take the tests.

- It's okay to guess. You won't lose any points if you're wrong.

- After you've finished the test, review the answer key to see where you went wrong.

*The hardest arithmetic to master is that which enables us to count our blessings. ~Eric Hoffer*

## PSAT Practice Tests Answer Sheet

Remove (or photocopy) the answer sheets and use it to complete the practice tests.

| | PSAT Practice Test 1 – Section 1 Answer Sheet | | | | |
|---|---|---|---|---|---|

1 (A) (B) (C) (D)   4 (A) (B) (C) (D)   7 (A) (B) (C) (D)   10 (A) (B) (C) (D)   13 (A) (B) (C) (D)

2 (A) (B) (C) (D)   5 (A) (B) (C) (D)   8 (A) (B) (C) (D)   11 (A) (B) (C) (D)

3 (A) (B) (C) (D)   6 (A) (B) (C) (D)   9 (A) (B) (C) (D)   12 (A) (B) (C) (D)

14      15      16      17

## PSAT Practice Test 1 – Section 2 Answer Sheet

1  Ⓐ Ⓑ Ⓒ Ⓓ   7  Ⓐ Ⓑ Ⓒ Ⓓ   13  Ⓐ Ⓑ Ⓒ Ⓓ   19  Ⓐ Ⓑ Ⓒ Ⓓ   25  Ⓐ Ⓑ Ⓒ Ⓓ

2  Ⓐ Ⓑ Ⓒ Ⓓ   8  Ⓐ Ⓑ Ⓒ Ⓓ   14  Ⓐ Ⓑ Ⓒ Ⓓ   20  Ⓐ Ⓑ Ⓒ Ⓓ   26  Ⓐ Ⓑ Ⓒ Ⓓ

3  Ⓐ Ⓑ Ⓒ Ⓓ   9  Ⓐ Ⓑ Ⓒ Ⓓ   15  Ⓐ Ⓑ Ⓒ Ⓓ   21  Ⓐ Ⓑ Ⓒ Ⓓ   27  Ⓐ Ⓑ Ⓒ Ⓓ

4  Ⓐ Ⓑ Ⓒ Ⓓ   10  Ⓐ Ⓑ Ⓒ Ⓓ   16  Ⓐ Ⓑ Ⓒ Ⓓ   22  Ⓐ Ⓑ Ⓒ Ⓓ

5  Ⓐ Ⓑ Ⓒ Ⓓ   11  Ⓐ Ⓑ Ⓒ Ⓓ   17  Ⓐ Ⓑ Ⓒ Ⓓ   23  Ⓐ Ⓑ Ⓒ Ⓓ

6  Ⓐ Ⓑ Ⓒ Ⓓ   12  Ⓐ Ⓑ Ⓒ Ⓓ   18  Ⓐ Ⓑ Ⓒ Ⓓ   24  Ⓐ Ⓑ Ⓒ Ⓓ

28        29        30        31

## PSAT Practice Test 2 – Section 1 Answer Sheet

1  Ⓐ Ⓑ Ⓒ Ⓓ    4  Ⓐ Ⓑ Ⓒ Ⓓ    7  Ⓐ Ⓑ Ⓒ Ⓓ    10  Ⓐ Ⓑ Ⓒ Ⓓ    13  Ⓐ Ⓑ Ⓒ Ⓓ

2  Ⓐ Ⓑ Ⓒ Ⓓ    5  Ⓐ Ⓑ Ⓒ Ⓓ    8  Ⓐ Ⓑ Ⓒ Ⓓ    11  Ⓐ Ⓑ Ⓒ Ⓓ

3  Ⓐ Ⓑ Ⓒ Ⓓ    6  Ⓐ Ⓑ Ⓒ Ⓓ    9  Ⓐ Ⓑ Ⓒ Ⓓ    12  Ⓐ Ⓑ Ⓒ Ⓓ

14

15

16

17

1  Ⓐ Ⓑ Ⓒ Ⓓ    7  Ⓐ Ⓑ Ⓒ Ⓓ    13  Ⓐ Ⓑ Ⓒ Ⓓ    19  Ⓐ Ⓑ Ⓒ Ⓓ    25  Ⓐ Ⓑ Ⓒ Ⓓ

2  Ⓐ Ⓑ Ⓒ Ⓓ    8  Ⓐ Ⓑ Ⓒ Ⓓ    14  Ⓐ Ⓑ Ⓒ Ⓓ    20  Ⓐ Ⓑ Ⓒ Ⓓ    26  Ⓐ Ⓑ Ⓒ Ⓓ

3  Ⓐ Ⓑ Ⓒ Ⓓ    9  Ⓐ Ⓑ Ⓒ Ⓓ    15  Ⓐ Ⓑ Ⓒ Ⓓ    21  Ⓐ Ⓑ Ⓒ Ⓓ    27  Ⓐ Ⓑ Ⓒ Ⓓ

4  Ⓐ Ⓑ Ⓒ Ⓓ    10  Ⓐ Ⓑ Ⓒ Ⓓ    16  Ⓐ Ⓑ Ⓒ Ⓓ    22  Ⓐ Ⓑ Ⓒ Ⓓ

5  Ⓐ Ⓑ Ⓒ Ⓓ    11  Ⓐ Ⓑ Ⓒ Ⓓ    17  Ⓐ Ⓑ Ⓒ Ⓓ    23  Ⓐ Ⓑ Ⓒ Ⓓ

6  Ⓐ Ⓑ Ⓒ Ⓓ    12  Ⓐ Ⓑ Ⓒ Ⓓ    18  Ⓐ Ⓑ Ⓒ Ⓓ    24  Ⓐ Ⓑ Ⓒ Ⓓ

28          29          30          31

# PSAT Math
# Practice Test 1

## Section 1

## (No Calculator)

**17 questions**

**Total time for this section:** 25 Minutes

*You MAY NOT use a calculator on this Section.*

## Reference Sheet

     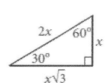 

$A = \pi r^2$       $A = \ell w$       $A = \frac{1}{2}bh$       $c^2 = a^2 + b^2$       Special Right Triangles

$C = 2\pi r$

$V = \ell w h$       $V = \pi r^2 h$       $V = \frac{4}{3}\pi r^3$       $V = \frac{1}{3}\pi r^2 h$       $V = \frac{1}{3}\ell w h$

The number of degrees of arc in a circle is 360.

The number of radians of arc in a circle is $2\pi$.

The sum of the measures in degrees of the angles of a triangle is 180.

1) John works for an electric company. He receives a monthly salary of $4,500 plus 5% of all his monthly sales as bonus. If $x$ is the number of all John's sales per month, which of the following represents John's monthly revenue in dollars?

    A. $0.05x$

    B. $0.95x - 4,500$

    C. $0.05x + 4,500$

    D. $0.95x + 4,500$

2) If $f(x^2) = 3x + 4$, for all positive value of $x$, what is the value of $f(121)$?

    A. 367

    B. 37

    C. 29

    D. $-29$

3) If $a$ and $b$ are solutions of the following equation, which of the following is the ratio $\frac{a}{b}$?

$(a > b)$

$$2x^2 - 11x + 8 = -3x + 18$$

    A. $\frac{1}{5}$

    B. $5$

    C. $-\frac{1}{5}$

    D. $-5$

4) A line in the $xy$-plane passes through origin and has a slope of $\frac{1}{3}$. Which of the following points lies on the line?

   A. $(2,1)$

   B. $(4,1)$

   C. $(9,3)$

   D. $(6,3)$

5) Which of the following is the solution of the following inequality?
$$2x + 4 > 11x - 12.5 - 3.5x$$

   A. $x < 3$

   B. $x > 3$

   C. $x \leq 4$

   D. $x \geq 4$

6) If $a$, $b$ and $c$ are positive integers and $3a = 4b = 5c$, then the value of $a + 2b + 15c$ is how many times the value of $a$?

   A. 11.5

   B. 12

   C. 12.5

   D. 15

7) If $x \neq -4$ and $x \neq 5$, which of the following is equivalent to $\dfrac{1}{\frac{1}{x-5}+\frac{1}{x+4}}$?

A. $\dfrac{(x-5)(x+4)}{(x-5)+(x+4)}$

B. $\dfrac{(x+4)+(x-5)}{(x+4)(x-5)}$

C. $\dfrac{(x+4)(x-5)}{(x+4)-(x+5)}$

D. $\dfrac{(x+4)+(x-5)}{(x+4)-(x-5)}$

| Gender | Under 45 | 45 or older | total |
|---|---|---|---|
| Male | 12 | 6 | 18 |
| Female | 5 | 7 | 12 |
| Total | 17 | 13 | 30 |

8) The table above shows the distribution of age and gender for 30 employees in a company. If one employee is selected at random, what is the probability that the employee selected be either a female under age 45 or a male age 45 or older?

A. $\dfrac{5}{6}$

B. $\dfrac{5}{30}$

C. $\dfrac{6}{30}$

D. $\dfrac{11}{30}$

9) If a parabola with equation $y = ax^2 + 5x + 10$, where $a$ is constant, passes through point (2, 12), what is the value of $a^2$?

   A. $-2$

   B. $2$

   C. $-4$

   D. $4$

10) What is the value of $f(5)$ for the following function $f$?

$$f(x) = x^2 - 3x$$

   A. $5$

   B. $10$

   C. $15$

   D. $20$

11) John buys a pepper plant that is 6 inches tall. With regular watering the plant grows 4 inches a year. Writing John's plant's height as a function of time, what does the $y-$intercept represent?

   A. The $y-$intercept represents the rate of grows of the plant which is 5 inches

   B. The $y-$intercept represents the starting height of 6 inches

   C. The $y-$intercept represents the rate of growth of plant which is 3 inches per year

   D. There is no $y-$intercept

12) What is the solution of the following system of equations?

$$\begin{cases} \dfrac{-x}{2} + \dfrac{y}{4} = 1 \\ \dfrac{-5y}{6} + 2x = 4 \end{cases}$$

A. $x = 48, y = 22$

B. $x = 50, y = 20$

C. $x = 20, y = 50$

D. $x = 22, y = 48$

13) What is the length of AB in the following figure if $AE = 4$, $CD = 6$ and $AC = 12$?

A. 3.8

B. 4.8

C. 7.2

D. 24

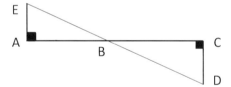

Questions 14–17 are grid-ins questions. Solve the problems and enter your answers in the grid on the answer sheet as shown below.

Answer: $\frac{6}{7}$

Answer: 3.72

Write answers in the boxes →

Grid in results

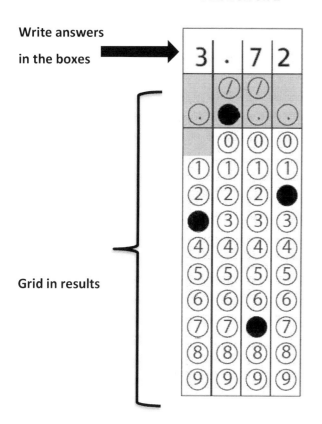

14) If $x \neq 0$, what is the value of $\dfrac{(10(x)(y^2))^2}{(8xy^2)^2}$?

15) In the following equation, what is the value of $y - 3x$?

$$\frac{y}{5} = x - \frac{2}{5}x + 10$$

16) What is the value of $x$ in the following equation?

$$\frac{x^2-9}{x+3} + 2(x+4) = 15$$

17) The length of a rectangle is 3 meters greater than 4 times its width. The perimeter of the rectangle is 36 meters. What is the area of the rectangle in meters?

# STOP

## This is the End of this Section. You may check your work on this section if you still have time.

# PSAT Math

# Practice Test 1

## Section 2

## (Calculator)

**31 questions**

**Total time for this section:** 45 Minutes

*You may use a scientific calculator on this Section.*

## Reference Sheet

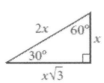

$A = \pi r^2$      $A = \ell w$      $A = \dfrac{1}{2}bh$      $c^2 = a^2 + b^2$      Special Right Triangles

$C = 2\pi r$

$V = \ell w h$      $V = \pi r^2 h$      $V = \dfrac{4}{3}\pi r^3$      $V = \dfrac{1}{3}\pi r^2 h$      $V = \dfrac{1}{3}\ell w h$

The number of degrees of arc in a circle is 360.

The number of radians of arc in a circle is $2\pi$.

The sum of the measures in degrees of the angles of a triangle is 180.

1) If $8 + 2x$ is 16 more than 20, what is the value of $6x$?

   A. 40

   B. 55

   C. 62

   D. 84

2) If a gas tank can hold 25 gallons, how many gallons does it contain when it is $\frac{2}{5}$ full?

   A. 50

   B. 125

   C. 62.5

   D. 10

3) In the $xy$-plane, the point $(4, 3)$ and $(3, 2)$ are on line A. Which of the following equations of lines is parallel to line A?

   A. $y = 3x$

   B. $y = \frac{x}{2}$

   C. $y = 2x$

   D. $y = x$

4) If $y = nx + 2$, where $n$ is a constant, and when $x = 6$, $y = 14$, what is the value of $y$ when $x = 10$?

    A. 10

    B. 12

    C. 18

    D. 22

5) A football team won exactly 80% of the games it played during last session. Which of the following could be the total number of games the team played last season?

    A. 49

    B. 35

    C. 12

    D. 32

6) The capacity of a red box is 20% bigger than the capacity of a blue box. If the red box can hold 30 equal sized books, how many of the same books can the blue box hold?

    A. 9

    B. 15

    C. 21

    D. 25

www.EffortlessMath.com

7) The sum of six different negative integers is $-70$. If the smallest of these integers is $-15$, what is the largest possible value of one of the other five integers?

   A. $-14$
   B. $-10$
   C. $-5$
   D. $-1$

8) If $x$ is greater than 0 and less than 1, which of the following is true?

   A. $x < \sqrt{x^2 + 1} < \sqrt{x^2} + 1$
   B. $x < \sqrt{x^2} + 1 < \sqrt{x^2 + 1}$
   C. $\sqrt{x^2 + 1} < x < \sqrt{x^2} + 1$
   D. $\sqrt{x^2} + 1 < \sqrt{x^2 + 1} < x$

## Questions 9 and 11 are based on the following data

*Types of air pollutions in 10 cities of a country*

| Type of Pollution | Number of Cities | | | | | | | | | |
|---|---|---|---|---|---|---|---|---|---|---|
| | 1 | 2 | 3 | 4 | 5 | 6 | 7 | 8 | 9 | 10 |
| A | █ | █ | █ | █ | █ | █ | | | | |
| B | █ | █ | █ | | | | | | | |
| C | █ | █ | █ | █ | | | | | | |
| D | █ | █ | █ | █ | █ | █ | █ | █ | █ | |
| E | █ | █ | █ | █ | █ | █ | █ | █ | | |

9) If $a$ is the mean (average) of the number of cities in each pollution type category, $b$ is the mode, and $c$ is the median of the number of cities in each pollution type category, then which of the following must be true?

A. $a < b < c$

B. $b < a < c$

C. $a = c$

D. $b < c = a$

10) What percent of cities are in the type of pollution A, C, and E respectively?

A. 60%, 40%, 90%

B. 30%, 40%, 90%

C. 30%, 40%, 60%

D. 40%, 60%, 90%

11) How many cities should be added to type of pollutions B until the ratio of cities in type of pollution B to cities in type of pollution E will be 0.625?

A. 2

B. 3

C. 4

D. 5

12) The ratio of boys and girls in a class is 4:7. If there are 44 students in the class, how many more boys should be enrolled to make the ratio 1:1?

A. 8

B. 10

C. 12

D. 16

13) In the following right triangle, if the sides AB and BC become twice longer, what will be the ratio of the perimeter of the triangle to its area?

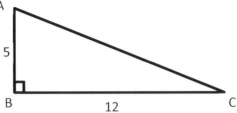

A.  $\frac{1}{2}$

B.  2

C.  $\frac{1}{3}$

D.  3

14) What is the ratio of the minimum value to the maximum value of the following function?

$$-2 \le x \le 3$$
$$f(x) = -3x + 1$$

A.  $\frac{7}{8}$

B.  $-\frac{8}{7}$

C.  $-\frac{7}{8}$

D.  $\frac{8}{7}$

## Questions 15 to 17 are based on the following data

*Number of Men and Women in four cities of a country*

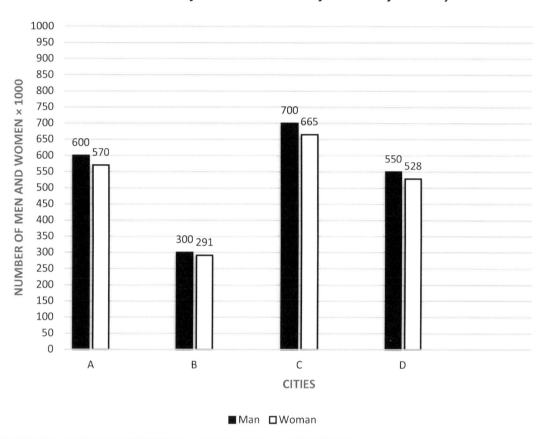

15) What's the maximum ratio of women to men in the four cities?

A. 0.98

B. 0.97

C. 0.96

D. 0.95

16) What's the ratio of percentage of men in city A to percentage of women in city C?

    A.  0.9

    B.  0.95

    C.  1

    D.  1.05

17) How many women should be added to city D until the ratio of women to men will be 1.2?

    A.  120

    B.  128

    C.  132

    D.  160

18) In the rectangle below if $y > 5$ cm and the area of rectangle is 50 cm$^2$ and the perimeter of the rectangle is 30 cm, what is the value of $x$ and $y$ respectively?

    A.  4, 11

    B.  5, 11

    C.  5, 10

    D.  4, 10

19) If a car has 80-liter petrol and after one hour driving the car use 6-liter petrol, how much petrol will remain after $x$-hours driving?

    A. $6x - 80$

    B. $80 + 6x$

    C. $80 - 6x$

    D. $80 - x$

20) In the triangle below, if the measure of angle $A$ is 37 degrees, then what is the value of $y$? (figure is NOT drawn to scale)

    A. 62

    B. 70

    C. 78

    D. 86

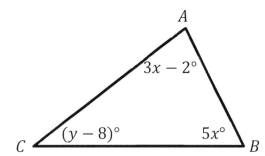

21) The following graph shows the mark of six students in mathematics. What is the mean (average) of the marks?

A. 15

B. 14.5

C. 14

D. 13.5

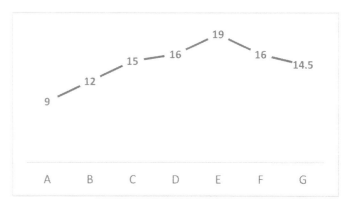

22) If $f(x) = 3x + 4(x + 1) + 2$ then $f(4x) =$?

A. $28x + 6$

B. $16x - 6$

C. $25x + 4$

D. $12x + 3$

23) Which of the following values for $x$ and $y$ satisfy the following system of equations?

$$\begin{cases} x + 4y = 10 \\ 5x + 10y = 20 \end{cases}$$

A. $x = 3, y = 2$

B. $x = 2, y - 3$

C. $x = -2, y = 3$

D. $x = 3, y = -2$

24) Given the right triangle ABC bellow, $\cos(\beta)$ is equal to?

A. $\frac{a}{b}$

B. $\frac{a}{\sqrt{a^2+b^2}}$

C. $\frac{\sqrt{a^2+b^2}}{ab}$

D. $\frac{b}{\sqrt{a^2+b^2}}$

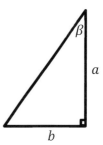

25) Solve the following inequality.

$$\left|\frac{x}{2} - 2x + 10\right| < 5$$

A. $-\frac{10}{3} < x < 10$

B. $-10 < x < \frac{10}{3}$

C. $\frac{10}{3} < x < 10$

D. $-10 < x < -\frac{10}{3}$

26) If $x$ is directly proportional to the square of $y$, and $y = 2$ when $x = 12$, then when $x = 75$

$y = ?$

A. $\frac{1}{5}$

B. 1

C. 5

D. 12

27) If $\frac{a-b}{b} = \frac{10}{11}$, then which of the following must be true?

   A. $\frac{a}{b} = \frac{11}{10}$

   B. $\frac{a}{b} = \frac{21}{11}$

   C. $\frac{a}{b} = \frac{11}{21}$

   D. $\frac{a}{b} = \frac{21}{10}$

## Grid-ins Questions

Questions 28–31 are grid-ins questions. Solve the problems and enter your answers in the grid

on the answer sheet as shown below.

Answer: $\dfrac{6}{7}$

Answer: 3.72

Write answers
in the boxes

Grid in results

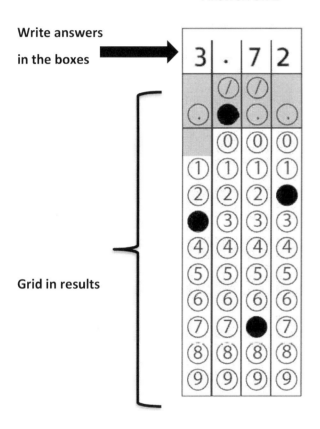

28) $f(x) = ax^2 + bx + c$ is a quadratic function where $a$, $b$ and $c$ are constant. The value of $x$

of the point of intersection of this quadratic function and linear function $g(x) = 2x - 3$ is

2. The vertex of $f(x)$ is at $(-2, 5)$. What is the product of $a$, $b$ and $c$?

29) A ladder leans against a wall forming a 60° angle between the ground and the ladder. If the bottom of the ladder is 45 feet away from the wall, how many feet is the ladder?

30) The volume of cube A is $\frac{1}{3}$ of its surface area. What is the length of an edge of cube A?

31) If $3x + 6y = \frac{-3y^2+15}{x}$, what is the value of $(x + y)^2$? $(x \neq 0)$

# STOP

## This is the End of this Section. You may check your work on this section if you still have time.

# PSAT Math

# Practice Test 2

## Section 1

## (No Calculator)

**17 questions**

**Total time for this section:** 25 Minutes

*You May NOT use a calculator on this Section.*

## Reference Sheet

$A = \pi r^2$        $A = \ell w$        $A = \dfrac{1}{2}bh$        $c^2 = a^2 + b^2$        Special Right Triangles

$C = 2\pi r$

$V = \ell w h$        $V = \pi r^2 h$        $V = \dfrac{4}{3}\pi r^3$        $V = \dfrac{1}{3}\pi r^2 h$        $V = \dfrac{1}{3}\ell w h$

The number of degrees of arc in a circle is 360.

The number of radians of arc in a circle is $2\pi$.

The sum of the measures in degrees of the angles of a triangle is 180.

1)  If $5x - 8 = 4.5$, what is the value of $3x + 3$ ?

    A.  10.5

    B.  12.5

    C.  15.5

    D.  25

2)  If the function f is defined by $f(x) = x^2 + 2x - 5$, which of the following is equivalent to $f(3t^2)$?

    A.  $3t^4 + 6t^2 - 5$

    B.  $9t^4 + 6t^2 - 5$

    C.  $3t^4 + 3t^2 - 5$

    D.  $3t^4 + 6t^2 + 5$

3)  If $xp + 2yq = 26$ and $xp + yq = 17$, what is the value of $yq$?

    A.  6

    B.  7

    C.  8

    D.  9

4) The circle graph below shows all Mr. Green's expenses for last month. If he spent $660 on his car, how much did he spend for his rent?

Mr. Green's monthly expenses

A. $700

B. $740

C. $780

D. $810

5) If $x^2 + 3$ and $x^2 - 3$ are two factors of the polynomial $12x^4 + n$ and $n$ is a constant, what is the value of $n$?

A. $-108$

B. $-24$

C. $24$

D. $108$

0.ABC          0.0D

6) The letters represent two decimals listed above. One of the decimals is equivalent to $\frac{1}{8}$ and the other is equivalent to $\frac{1}{20}$. What is the product of C and D?

A. 0

B. 5

C. 25

D. 20

7) In the diagram below, circle A represents the set of all odd numbers, circle B represents the set of all negative numbers, and circle C represents the set of all multiples of 5. Which number could be replaced with $y$?

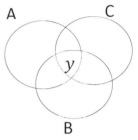

A. 5

B. 0

C. $-5$

D. $-10$

8) There are only red and blue cards in a box. The probability of choosing a red card in the box at random is one third. If there are 246 blue cards, how many cards are in the box?

A. 123

B. 308

C. 328

D. 369

9) Both $(x = -2)$ and $(x = 3)$ are solutions for which of the following equations?

      I.    $x^2 - x + 6 = 0$

      II.    $2x^2 - 2x = 12$

      III.    $5x^2 - 5x - 30 = 0$

A. II only

B. I and II

C. II and III

D. I, II and III

10) The radius of circle A is three times the radius of circle B. If the circumference of circle A is $18\pi$, what is the area of circle B?

    A.  $3\pi$

    B.  $6\pi$

    C.  $9\pi$

    D.  $12\pi$

11) In a certain bookshelf of a library, there are 35 biology books, 95 history books, and 80 language books. What is the ratio of the number of biology books to the total number of books in this bookshelf?

    A.  $\dfrac{1}{4}$

    B.  $\dfrac{1}{6}$

    C.  $\dfrac{2}{7}$

    D.  $\dfrac{3}{8}$

12) In the figure below, what is the value of $x$?

    A.  43

    B.  67

    C.  77

    D.  90

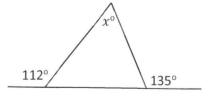

13) The following table represents the value of $x$ and function $f(x)$. Which of the following could be the equation of the function $f(x)$?

| $x$ | $f(x)$ |
|-----|--------|
| 1 | 5 |
| 4 | 6 |
| 9 | 7 |
| 16 | 8 |

A. $f(x) = x^2 - 5$

B. $f(x) = x^2 - 1$

C. $f(x) = \sqrt{x + 2}$

D. $f(x) = \sqrt{x} + 4$

## Grid-ins Questions

Questions 14–17 are grid-ins questions. Solve the problems and enter your answers in the grid on the answer sheet as shown below.

Answer: $\dfrac{6}{7}$

Answer: 3.72

Write answers in the boxes

Grid in results

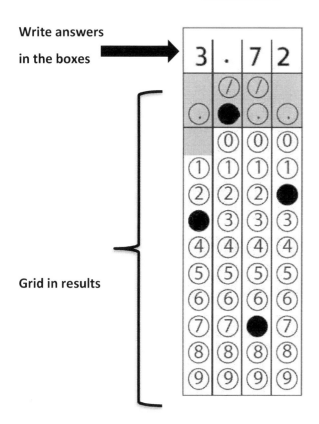

14) Michelle and Alec can finish a job together in 100 minutes. If Michelle can do the job by herself in 5 hours, how many minutes does it take Alec to finish the job?

15) In the following figure, point O is the center of the circle and the equilateral triangle has perimeter 33. What is the circumference of the circle? ($\pi = 3$)

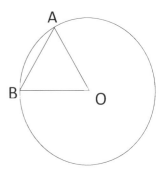

16) If 12% of $x$ is 72 and $\frac{1}{8}$ of $y$ is 16, what is the value of $x - y$ ?

17) Angle $a$ is 630 degrees and can be written $x\pi$ in radian. What is the value of $x$?

# STOP

**This is the End of this Section. You may check your work on this section if you still have time.**

# PSAT Math

# Practice Test 2

## Section 2

## (Calculator)

**31 questions**

**Total time for this section:** 45 Minutes

*You can use a scientific calculator on this Section.*

## Reference Sheet

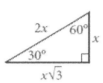

$A = \pi r^2$       $A = \ell w$       $A = \frac{1}{2}bh$       $c^2 = a^2 + b^2$       Special Right Triangles

$C = 2\pi r$

$V = \ell wh$       $V = \pi r^2 h$       $V = \frac{4}{3}\pi r^3$       $V = \frac{1}{3}\pi r^2 h$       $V = \frac{1}{3}\ell wh$

The number of degrees of arc in a circle is 360.

The number of radians of arc in a circle is $2\pi$.

The sum of the measures in degrees of the angles of a triangle is 180.

1) What is the value of $\frac{3a-2}{2}$, if $-3a + 5a + 7a = 45$ ?

   A. 6.5

   B. 6

   C. 5.5

   D. 5

2) What is the average (arithmetic mean) of all integers from 11 to 19?

   A. 14

   B. 14.5

   C. 15

   D. 15.5

3) What is the value of $|-12 - 5| - |-8 + 2|$?

   A. 11

   B. $-11$

   C. 23

   D. $-23$

4) The table represents different values of function $g(x)$. What is the value of

   $3g(-2) - 2g(3)$?

A.  $-12$

B.  $-2$

C.  3

D.  13

| $x$ | $g(x)$ |
|-----|--------|
| -2  | 3      |
| -1  | 2      |
| 0   | 1      |
| 1   | 0      |
| 2   | -1     |
| 3   | -2     |

5) A container holds 3.5 gallons of water when it is $\frac{7}{24}$ full. How many gallons of water does the container hold when it's full?

A.  8

B.  12

C.  16

D.  20

6) On the following figure, what is the area of the quadrilateral ABCD?

A. 27

B. 30

C. 33

D. 36

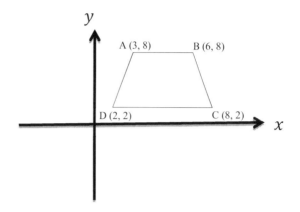

7) If $a$ is an odd integer divisible by 5. Which of the following must be divisible by 4?

A. $a - 1$

B. $a + 1$

C. $2a$

D. $2a - 2$

8) If $(3^a)^b = 81$, then what is the value of $ab$?

A. 2

B. 3

C. 4

D. 5

## Questions 9 to 11 are based on the following data

*Number of clothes sold in a clothing store*

9) Between which two of the months shown was there a twenty percent decreased in the number of pants sold?

A. January and February
B. February and March
C. March and April
D. April and May

10) During the six-month period shown, what is the median number of shirts and mean number of shoes per month?

    A. 146.5, 30

    B. 147.5, 29

    C. 146.5, 31

    D. 147.5, 30

11) How many shoes need to be added in April until the ratio of number of pants to number of shoes in April equals to five-seventeenth of this ratio in May?

    A. 90

    B. 80

    C. 60

    D. 50

12) What is the $x$-intercept of the line with equation $2x - 2y = 5$?

    A. $-5$

    B. $-2$

    C. $\dfrac{5}{2}$

    D. $\dfrac{5}{4}$

13) The perimeter of a triangle is 10 cm and the lengths of its sides are different integers. What is the greatest possible value of the biggest side?

A.  4 cm

B.  5 cm

C.  6 cm

D.  7 cm

14) If $(x - 2)^3 = 27$ which of the following could be the value of $(x - 4)(x - 3)$?

A.  1

B.  2

C.  $-1$

D.  $-2$

A library has 840 books that include Mathematics, Physics, Chemistry, English and History.

Use following graph to answer questions 15 to 17.

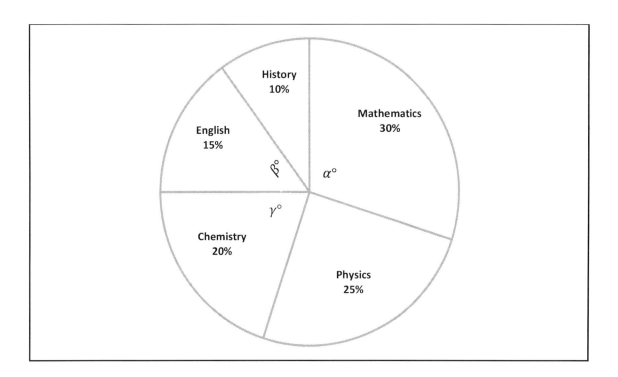

15) What is the product of the number of Mathematics and number of English books?

    A. 21,168

    B. 31,752

    C. 26,460

    D. 17,640

16) What are the values of angle $\alpha$ and $\beta$ respectively?

    A.  90°, 54°

    B.  120°, 36°

    C.  120°, 45°

    D.  108°, 54°

17) The librarians decided to move some of the books in the Mathematics section to Chemistry section. How many books are in the Chemistry section if now $\gamma = \frac{2}{5}\alpha$?

    A.  80

    B.  120

    C.  150

    D.  180

18) In 1999, the average worker's income increased \$2,000 per year starting from \$24,000 annual salary. Which equation represents income greater than average? (I = income, x = number of years after 1999)

    A.  $I > 2000\,x + 24000$

    B.  $I > -\,2000\,x + 24000$

    C.  $I < -\,2000\,x + 24000$

    D.  $I < 2000\,x - 24000$

19) The Jackson Library is ordering some bookshelves. If $x$ is the number of bookshelf the library wants to order, which each costs $100 and there is a one-time delivery charge of $800, which of the following represents the total cost, in dollar, per bookshelf?

    A. $100x + 800$

    B. $100 + 800x$

    C. $\dfrac{100x + 80}{100}$

    D. $\dfrac{100x + 800}{x}$

20) What is the sum of $\sqrt{x-7}$ and $\sqrt{x}-7$ when $\sqrt{x}=4$ ?

    A. $-3$

    B. $-1$

    C. $0$

    D. $3$

21) In the following figure, point Q lies on line n, what is the value of $y$ if $x = 35$?

    A. 15

    B. 25

    C. 35

    D. 45

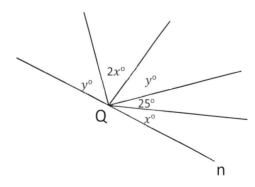

22) In the following figure, AB is the diameter of the circle. What is the circumference of the circle?

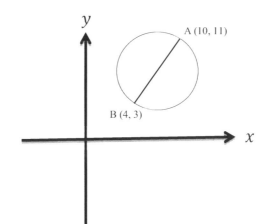

A. $5\pi$

B. $10\pi$

C. $15\pi$

D. $20\pi$

23) What is the smallest integer whose square root is greater than 6?

A. 16

B. 25

C. 37

D. 49

24) If the area of trapezoid is 126 cm, what is the perimeter of the trapezoid?

A. 12 cm

B. 32 cm

C. 46 cm

D. 55 cm

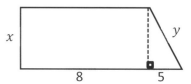

25) What is the solution of the following inequality?

$$|x - 2| \geq 3$$

A. $x \geq 5 \cup x \leq -1$

B. $-1 \leq x \leq 5$

C. $x \geq 5$

D. $x \leq -1$

26) If the area of the following rectangular ABCD is 100, and E is the midpoint of AB, what is the area of the shaded part?

A. 25

B. 50

C. 75

D. 80

27) Which of the following is equivalent to $13 < -3x - 2 < 22$ ?

A. $-8 < x < -5$

B. $5 < x < 8$

C. $\frac{11}{3} < x < \frac{20}{3}$

D. $\frac{-20}{3} < x < \frac{-11}{3}$

## Grid-ins Questions

Questions 28–31 are grid-ins questions. Solve the problems and enter your answers in the grid on the answer sheet as shown below.

Answer: $\frac{6}{7}$

Answer: 3.72

Write answers in the boxes →

Grid in results

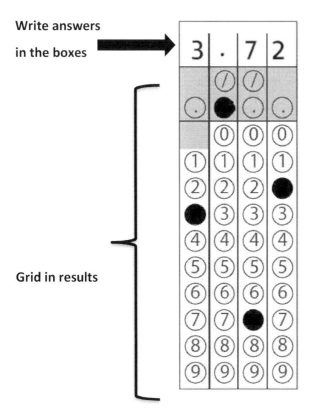

28) In the following figure, ABCD is a rectangle. If $a = \sqrt{3}$, and $b = 2a$, find the area of the

shaded region? (the shaded region is a trapezoid) (Round your answer to the nearest

hundredths place)

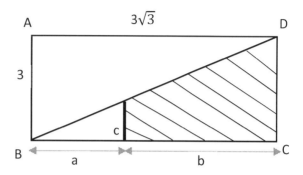

29) If $sin\ A\ =\ \frac{1}{3}$ in a right triangle and the angle A is an acute angle, then what is $cos\ A$?

(Round your answer to the nearest hundredths place)

30) 6 liters of water are poured into an aquarium that's 15cm long, 5cm wide, and 60cm high. How many cm will the water level in the aquarium rise due to this added water? (1 liter of water = 1000 cm3)?

31) If $x \begin{bmatrix} 2 & 0 \\ 0 & 4 \end{bmatrix} = \begin{bmatrix} x + 3y - 5 & 0 \\ 0 & 2y + 10 \end{bmatrix}$, what is the product of $x$ and $y$?

# STOP

## This is the End of this Section. You may check your work on this section if you still have time.

# PSAT Math Practice Tests Answers and Explanations

✳ Now, it's time to review your results to see where you went wrong and what areas you need to improve!

| PSAT Math Practice Test 1 | | | | | | | |
|---|---|---|---|---|---|---|---|
| **Section 1 – No Calculator** | | | | **Section 2 - Calculator** | | | |
| 1- | **C** | 11- | **B** | 1- | **D** | 17- | **C** |
| 2- | **B** | 12- | **D** | 2- | **D** | 18- | **C** |
| 3- | **D** | 13- | **B** | 3- | **D** | 19- | **C** |
| 4- | **C** | 14- | **25/16** | 4- | **D** | 20- | **B** |
| 5- | **A** | 15- | **50** | 5- | **B** | 21- | **B** |
| 6- | **A** | 16- | **10/3** | 6- | **D** | 22- | **A** |
| 7- | **C** | 17- | **45** | 7- | **C** | 23- | **C** |
| 8- | **A** | | | 8- | **A** | 24- | **B** |
| 9- | **D** | | | 9- | **C** | 25- | **C** |
| 10- | **B** | | | 10- | **A** | 26- | **C** |
| | | | | 11- | **A** | 27- | **B** |
| | | | | 12- | **C** | 28- | **1** |
| | | | | 13- | **A** | 29- | **90** |
| | | | | 14- | **B** | 30- | **2** |
| | | | | 15- | **B** | 31- | **5** |
| | | | | 16- | **D** | | |

| PSAT Math Practice Test 2 | | | | | | | |
|---|---|---|---|---|---|---|---|
| Section 1 – No Calculator | | | | Section 2 - Calculator | | | |
| 1- | A | 11- | B | 1- | A | 17- | B |
| 2- | B | 12- | B | 2- | C | 18- | A |
| 3- | D | 13- | D | 3- | A | 19- | C |
| 4- | D | 14- | 150 | 4- | D | 20- | C |
| 5- | A | 15- | 66 | 5- | B | 21- | B |
| 6- | C | 16- | 472 | 6- | A | 22- | B |
| 7- | C | 17- | 3.5 | 7- | D | 23- | C |
| 8- | D | | | 8- | C | 24- | C |
| 9- | C | | | 9- | A | 25- | A |
| 10- | C | | | 10- | D | 26- | B |
| | | | | 11- | D | 27- | A |
| | | | | 12- | C | 28- | 6.93 |
| | | | | 13- | A | 29- | 0.94 |
| | | | | 14- | B | 30- | 80 |
| | | | | 15- | B | 31- | 12 |
| | | | | 16- | D | | |

# PSAT Math Practice Tests

# Explanations

## PSAT Math Practice Test 1

## Section 1 – No Calculator

1) **Choice C is correct**

$x$ is the number of all John's sales per month and 5% of it is:

$$5\% \times x = 0.05x$$

John's monthly revenue: $0.05x + 4,500$

2) **Choice D is correct**

$x^2 = 121 \rightarrow x = 11$ (positive value)    Or    $x = -11$ (negative value)

Since $x$ is positive, then:

$$f(121) = f(11^2) = 3(11) + 4 = 33 + 4 = 37$$

3) **Choice D is correct**

$$2x^2 - 11x + 8 = -3x + 18 \rightarrow 2x^2 - 11x + 3x + 8 - 18 = 0 \rightarrow 2x^2 - 8x - 10 = 0$$

$$\rightarrow 2(x^2 - 4x - 5) = 0 \rightarrow \text{Divide both sides by 2. Then:}$$

$x^2 - 4x - 5 = 0$, Find the factors of the quadratic equation.

$\rightarrow (x-5)(x+1)=0 \rightarrow x=5$ or $x=-1$

$a>b$, then: $a=5$ and $b=-1$

$$\frac{a}{b}=\frac{5}{-1}=-5$$

### 4) Choice C is correct

First, find the equation of the line. All lines through the origin are of the form $y=mx$, so the equation is $y=\frac{1}{3}x$. Of the given choices, only choice C (9,3), satisfies this equation:

$$y=\frac{1}{3}x \rightarrow 3=\frac{1}{3}(9)=3$$

### 5) Choice A is correct

$2x+4>11x-12.5-3.5x \rightarrow$ Combine like terms:

$2x+4>7.5x-12.5 \rightarrow$ Subtract $2x$ from both sides: $4>5.5x-12.5$

Add 12.5 both sides of the inequality.

$16.5>5.5x$, Divide both sides by 5.5.

$$\frac{16.5}{5.5}>x \rightarrow x<3$$

### 6) Choice A is correct

$3a=4b \rightarrow b=\frac{3a}{4}$ and $3a=5c \rightarrow c=\frac{3a}{5}$

$$a+2b+15c=a+\left(2\times\frac{3a}{4}\right)+\left(15\times\frac{3a}{5}\right)=a+1.5a+9a=11.5a$$

The value of $a+2b+15c$ is 11.5 times the value of $a$.

### 7) Choice A is correct

To rewrite $\dfrac{1}{\frac{1}{x-5}+\frac{1}{x+4}}$, first simplify $\dfrac{1}{x-5}+\dfrac{1}{x+4}$.

$$\frac{1}{x-5}+\frac{1}{x+4}=\frac{1(x+4)}{(x-5)(x+4)}+\frac{1(x-5)}{(x+4)(x-5)}=\frac{(x+4)+(x-5)}{(x+4)(x-5)}$$

Then:

$$\frac{1}{\frac{1}{x-5}+\frac{1}{x+4}}=\frac{1}{\frac{(x+4)+(x-5)}{(x+4)(x-5)}}=\frac{(x-5)(x+4)}{(x-5)+(x+4)}. \text{ (Remember, } \frac{1}{\frac{1}{x}}=x)$$

This result is equivalent to the expression in choice A.

## 8) Choice D is correct

Of the 30 employees, there are 5 females under age 45 and 6 males age 45 or older. Therefore, the probability that the person selected will be either a female under age 45 or a male age 45 or older is: $\dfrac{5}{30}+\dfrac{6}{30}=\dfrac{11}{30}$

## 9) Choice D is correct

Plug in the values of $x$ and $y$ of the point (2, 12) in the equation of the parabola. Then:

$$12=a(2)^2+5(2)+10 \rightarrow 12=4a+10+10 \rightarrow 12=4a+20$$

$$\rightarrow 4a=12-20=-8 \rightarrow a=\frac{-8}{4}=-2 \rightarrow a^2=(-2)^2=4$$

## 10) Choice B is correct

The input value is 5. Then: $x=5$

$$f(x)=x^2-3x \rightarrow f(5)=5^2-3(5)=25-15=10$$

## 11) Choice B is correct

To solve this problem, first recall the equation of a line: $y=mx+b$

Where, $m=slope$ and $y=y-intercept$

Remember that slope is the rate of change that occurs in a function and that the $y-$intercept is the $y$ value corresponding to $x = 0$.

Since the height of John's plant is 6 inches tall when he gets it. Time (or $x$) is zero. The plant grows 4 inches per year. Therefore, the rate of change of the plant's height is 4. The $y-$intercept represents the starting height of the plant which is 6 inches.

**12) Choice D is correct**

$$\begin{cases} \frac{-x}{2} + \frac{y}{4} = 1 \\ \frac{-5y}{6} + 2x = 4 \end{cases} \rightarrow \quad \text{Multiply the top equation by 4. Then,}$$

$$\begin{cases} -2x + y = 4 \\ \frac{-5y}{6} + 2x = 4 \end{cases} \rightarrow \quad \text{Add two equations.}$$

$\frac{1}{6}y = 8 \rightarrow y = 48$ , plug in the value of y into the first equation $\quad \rightarrow x = 22$

**13) Choice B is correct**

Two triangles $\Delta BAE$ and $\Delta BCD$ are similar. Then:

$$\frac{AE}{CD} = \frac{AB}{BC} \rightarrow \frac{4}{6} = \frac{x}{12} \rightarrow 48 - 4x = 6x \rightarrow 10x = 48 \rightarrow x = 4.8$$

**14) The answer is $\frac{25}{16}$**

First, simplify the numerator and the denominator.

$$\frac{(10(x)(y^2)^2}{(8xy^2)^2} = \frac{100x^2y^4}{64x^2y^4}$$

Remove $x^2y^4$ from both numerator and denominator.

$$\frac{100x^2y^4}{64x^2y^4} = \frac{100}{64} = \frac{25}{16}$$

**15) The answer is 50**

$\frac{y}{5} = x - \frac{2}{5}x + 10$, Multiply both sides of the equation by 5. Then:

$$5 \times \frac{y}{5} = 5 \times \left(x - \frac{2}{5}x + 10\right) \rightarrow y = 5x - 2x + 50 \rightarrow y = 3x + 50$$

Now, subtract $3x$ from both sides of the equation. Then:

$$y - 3x = 50$$

**16) The answer is $\frac{10}{3}$**

First, factorize the numerator and simplify.

$$\frac{x^2 - 9}{x + 3} + 2(x + 4) = 15 \rightarrow \frac{(x - 3)(x + 3)}{x + 3} + 2x + 8 = 15$$

Divide both sides of the fraction by $(x + 3)$. Then:

$$x - 3 + 2x + 8 = 15 \rightarrow 3x + 5 = 15$$

Subtract 5 from both sides of the equation. Then:

$$\rightarrow 3x = 15 - 5 = 10 \rightarrow x = \frac{10}{3}$$

**17) The answer is 45**

Let $L$ be the length of the rectangular and $W$ be the with of the rectangular. Then,

$$L = 4W + 3$$

The perimeter of the rectangle is 36 meters. Therefore:

$$2L + 2W = 36$$

$$L + W = 18$$

Replace the value of $L$ from the first equation into the second equation and solve for $W$:

$$(4W + 3) + W = 18 \rightarrow 5W + 3 = 18 \rightarrow 5W = 15 \rightarrow W = 3$$

The width of the rectangle is 3 meters and its length is:

$$L = 4W + 3 = 4(3) + 3 = 15$$

The area of the rectangle is: length × width = 3 × 15 = 45

# Section 2 –Calculator

**1) Choice D is correct**

The description $8 + 2x$ *is* 16 more than 20 can be written as the equation $8 + 2x = 16 + 20$, which is equivalent to $8 + 2x = 36$. Subtracting 8 from each side of $8 + 2x = 36$ gives

$2x = 28$. Since $6x$ is 3 times $2x$, multiplying both sides of $2x = 28$ by 3 gives $6x = 84$

**2) Choice D is correct**

$$\frac{2}{5} \times 25 = \frac{50}{5} = 10$$

**3) Choice D is correct**

The slop of line A is: $m = \frac{y_2 - y_1}{x_2 - x_1} = \frac{3-2}{4-3} = 1$

Parallel lines have the same slope and only choice D $(y = x)$ has slope of 1.

**4) Choice D is correct**

Substituting 6 for $x$ and 14 for $y$ in $y = nx + 2$ gives $14 = (n)(6) + 2$,

which gives $n = 2$. Hence, $y = 2x + 2$. Therefore, when $x = 10$, the value of $y$ is

$$y = (2)(10) + 2 = 22$$

**5) Choice B is correct**

Choices A, C and D are incorrect because 80% of each of the numbers is a non-whole number.

A. 49, $\qquad$ $80\% \ of \ 49 \ = \ 0.80 \times 49 = 39.2$

B. 35, $\qquad$ $80\% \ of \ 35 = 0.80 \times 35 = 28$

C. 12, $\qquad$ $80\% \ of \ 12 = 0.80 \times 12 = 9.6$

D. 32, $\qquad$ $80\% \ of \ 32 = 0.80 \times 32 = 25.6$

Only choice B gives a whole number.

### 6) Choice D is correct

The capacity of a red box is 20% bigger than the capacity of a blue box and it can hold 30 books. Therefore, we want to find a number that 20% bigger than that number is 30. Let $x$ be that number. Then:

$1.20 \times x = 30$, Divide both sides of the equation by 1.2. Then:

$$x = \frac{30}{1.20} = 25$$

### 7) Choice C is correct

The smallest number is $-15$. To find the largest possible value of one of the other five integers, we need to choose the smallest possible integers for four of them. Let $x$ be the largest number. Then:

$$-70 = (-15) + (-14) + (-13) + (-12) + (-11) + x \rightarrow -70 = -65 + x$$

$$\rightarrow x = -70 + 65 = -5$$

### 8) Choice A is correct

Let $x$ be equal to 0.5, then: $\quad x = 0.5$

$$\sqrt{x^2 + 1} = \sqrt{0.5^2 + 1} = \sqrt{1.25} \approx 1.12$$

$$\sqrt{x^2} + 1 = \sqrt{0.5^2} + 1 = 0.5 + 1 = 1.5$$

Then, option A is correct.

$$x < \sqrt{x^2 + 1} < \sqrt{x^2} + 1$$

### 9) Choice C is correct

Let's find the mean (average), mode and median of the number of cities for each type of pollution.

Number of cities for each type of pollution: 6, 3, 4, 9, 8

$$average \ (mean) = \frac{sum \ of \ terms}{number \ of \ terms} = \frac{6+3+4+9+8}{5} = \frac{30}{5} = 6$$

Median is the number in the middle. To find median, first list numbers in order from smallest to largest.

3, 4, 6, 8, 9

Median of the data is 6.

Mode is the number which appears most often in a set of numbers. Therefore, there is no mode in the set of numbers.

Median = Mean, then, $a=c$

### 10) Choice A is correct

Percent of cities in the type of pollution A: $\frac{6}{10} \times 100 = 60\%$

Percent of cities in the type of pollution C: $\frac{4}{10} \times 100 = 40\%$

Percent of cities in the type of pollution E: $\frac{9}{10} \times 100 = 90\%$

### 11) Choice A is correct

Let $x$ be the number of cities need to be added to type of pollutions B. Then:

$$\frac{x+3}{8} = 0.625 \rightarrow x + 3 = 8 \times 0.625 \rightarrow x + 3 = 5 \rightarrow x = 2$$

## 12) Choice C is correct

The ratio of boy to girls is 4:7. Therefore, there are 4 boys out of 11 students. To find the answer, first divide the total number of students by 11, then multiply the result by 4.

$44 \div 11 = 4 \Rightarrow 4 \times 4 = 16$

There are 16 boys and 28 (44 − 16) girls. So, 12 more boys should be enrolled to make the ratio 1:1

## 13) Choice A is correct

$AB = 5$    And    $BC = 12$

$AC = \sqrt{12^2 + 5^2} = \sqrt{144 + 25} = \sqrt{169} = 13$

Perimeter $= 5 + 12 + 13 = 30$

Area $= \frac{5 \times 12}{2} = 5 \times 6 = 30$

In this case, the ratio of the perimeter of the triangle to its area is: $\frac{30}{30} = 1$

If the sides AB and BC become twice longer, then:

$AB = 24$    And    $AC = 10$

$BC = \sqrt{24^2 + 10^2} = \sqrt{576 + 100} = \sqrt{676} = 26$

Perimeter $= 26 + 24 + 10 = 60$

Area $= \frac{10 \times 24}{2} = 10 \times 12 = 120$

In this case the ratio of the perimeter of the triangle to its area is: $\frac{60}{120} = \frac{1}{2}$

## 14) Choice B is correct

Since $f(x)$ is linear function with a negative slop, then when $x = -2, f(x)$ is maximum and when $x = 3, f(x)$ is minimum. Then the ratio of the minimum value to the maximum value of the function is: $\frac{f(3)}{f(-2)} = \frac{-3(3)+1}{-3(-2)+1} = \frac{-8}{7} = -\frac{8}{7}$

**15) Choice B is correct**

Ratio of women to men in city A: $\frac{570}{600} = 0.95$

Ratio of women to men in city B: $\frac{291}{300} = 0.97$

Ratio of women to men in city C: $\frac{665}{700} = 0.95$

Ratio of women to men in city D: $\frac{528}{550} = 0.96$

Choice B provides the maximum ratio of women to men in the four cities.

**16) Choice D is correct**

Percentage of men in city A $= \frac{600}{1170} \times 100 = 51.28\%$

Percentage of women in city C $= \frac{665}{1365} \times 100 = 48.72\%$

Percentage of men in city A to percentage of women in city C $= \frac{51.28}{48.72} = 1.05$

**17) Choice C is correct**

Let the number of women should be added to city D be $x$, then:

$\frac{528 + x}{550} = 1.2 \rightarrow 528 + x = 550 \times 1.2 = 660 \rightarrow x = 132$

**18) Choice C is correct**

The perimeter of the rectangle is: $2x + 2y = 30 \rightarrow x + y = 15 \rightarrow x = 15 - y$

The area of the rectangle is: $x \times y = 50 \rightarrow (15 - y)(y) = 50 \rightarrow y^2 - 15y + 50 = 0$

Solve the quadratic equation by factoring method.

$(y - 5)(y - 10) = 0 \rightarrow y = 5$ (Unacceptable, because $y$ must be greater than 5) or $y = 10$

If $y = 10 \rightarrow x \times y = 50 \rightarrow x \times 10 = 50 \rightarrow x = 5$

**19) Choice C is correct**

The amount of petrol consumed after $x$ hours is:   $6 \times x = 6x$

Petrol remaining after $x$ hours driving:     $80 - 6x$

**20) Choice D is correct**

In the figure angle $A$ is labeled $(3x - 2)$ and it measures 37. Thus, $3x - 2 = 37$ and $3x = 39$ or $x = 13$.

That means that angle $B$, which is labeled $(5x)$, must measure $5 \times 13 = 65$.

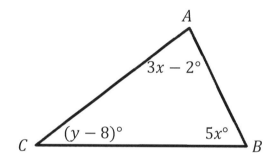

Since the three angles of a triangle must add up to 180, $37 + 65 + y - 8 = 180$, then:

$$y + 94 = 108 \rightarrow y = 180 - 94 = 86$$

**21) Choice B is correct**

$$average \ (mean) = \frac{sum \ of \ terms}{number \ of \ terms} = \frac{9 + 12 + 15 + 16 + 19 + 16 + 14.5}{7} = 14.5$$

**22) Choice A is correct**

If $f(x) = 3x + 4(x + 1) + 2$, then find $f(4x)$ by substituting $4x$ for every $x$ in the function. This gives:

$$f(4x) = 3(4x) + 4(4x + 1) + 2,$$

It simplifies to:

$$f(4x) = 3(4x) + 4(4x + 1) + 2 = 12x + 16x + 4 + 2 = 28x + 6$$

**23) Choice C is correct**

$\begin{cases} x + 4y = 10 \\ 5x + 10y = 20 \end{cases} \rightarrow$   Multiply the top equation by $-5$ then,

$\begin{cases} -5x - 20y = -50 \\ 5x + 10y = 20 \end{cases} \rightarrow$      Add two equations

$-10y = -30 \rightarrow y = 3$ , plug in the value of $y$ into the first equation

$$x + 4y = 10 \rightarrow x + 4(3) = 10 \rightarrow x + 12 = 10$$

Subtract 12 from both sides of the equation. Then:

$$x + 12 = 10 \rightarrow x = -2$$

**24) Choice B is correct**

$$\text{Cos}\,\beta = \frac{Adjacent\ side}{hypotenuse}$$

To find the hypotenuse, we need to use Pythagorean theorem.

$a^2 + b^2 = c^2 \rightarrow c = \sqrt{a^2 + b^2}$

$\cos(\beta) = \dfrac{a}{c} = \dfrac{a}{\sqrt{a^2 + b^2}}$

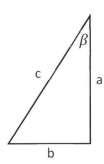

**25) Choice C is correct**

$\left|\dfrac{x}{2} - 2x + 10\right| < 5 \rightarrow \left|-\dfrac{3}{2}x + 10\right| < 5 \rightarrow -5 < -\dfrac{3}{2}x + 10 < 5$

Subtract 10 from all sides of the inequality.

$\rightarrow -5 - 10 < -\dfrac{3}{2}x + 10 - 10 < 5 - 10 \rightarrow -15 < -\dfrac{3}{2}x < -5$

Multiply all sides by 2.

$\rightarrow 2 \times (-15) < 2 \times \left(-\dfrac{3x}{2}\right) < 2 \times (-5) \rightarrow -30 < -3x < -10$

Divide all sides by $-3$. (Remember that when you divide all sides of an inequality by a negative number, the inequality sing will be swapped. $<$ becomes $>$)

$$\rightarrow \frac{-30}{-3} > \frac{-3x}{-3} > \frac{-10}{-3}$$

$$\rightarrow 10 > x > \frac{10}{3} \rightarrow \frac{10}{3} < x < 10$$

**26) Choice C is correct**

$x$ is directly proportional to the square of $y$. Then:

$$x = cy^2$$

$$12 = c(2)^2 \rightarrow 12 = 4c \rightarrow c = \frac{12}{4} = 3$$

The relationship between $x$ and $y$ is:

$$x = 3y^2$$

$$x = 75$$

$$75 = 3y^2 \rightarrow y^2 = \frac{75}{3} = 25 \rightarrow y = 5$$

**27) Choice B is correct**

The equation $\frac{a-b}{b} = \frac{10}{11}$ can be rewritten as $\frac{a}{b} - \frac{b}{b} = \frac{10}{11}$, from which it follows that $\frac{a}{b} - 1 = \frac{10}{11}$, or $\frac{a}{b} = \frac{10}{11} + 1 = \frac{21}{11}$.

**28) The answer is 1**

The intersection of two functions is the point with 2 for $x$. Then:

$$f(2) = g(2) \quad \text{and} \quad g(2) = (2 \times (2)) - 3 = 4 - 3 = 1$$

Then, $f(2) = 1 \rightarrow a(2)^2 + b(2) + c = 1 \rightarrow 4a + 2b + c = 1$ $\quad$ (i)

The value of $x$ in the vertex of the parabola is: $x = -\frac{b}{2a} \rightarrow -2 = -\frac{b}{2a} \rightarrow b = 4a$          (ii)

In the point $(-2, 5)$, the value of the $f(x)$ is 5.

$f(-2) = 5 \rightarrow a(-2)^2 + b(-2) + c = 5 \rightarrow 4a - 2b + c = 5$          (iii)

Using the first two equation:

$$\begin{cases} 4a + 2b + c = 1 \\ 4a - 2b + c = 5 \end{cases} \rightarrow$$

Equation 1 minus equation 2 is:

(i)−(iii) $\rightarrow 4b = -4 \rightarrow b = -1$          (iv)

Plug in the value of $b$ in the second equation:

$b = 4a \rightarrow a = \frac{b}{4} = -\frac{1}{4}$

Plug in the values of a and be in the first equation. Then:

$$\rightarrow 4\left(\frac{-1}{4}\right) + 2(-1) + c = 1 \rightarrow -1 - 2 + c = 1 \rightarrow c = 1 + 3 \rightarrow c = 4$$

The product of $a$, $b$ and $c = \left(-\frac{1}{4}\right) \times (-1) \times 4 = 1$

**29) The answer is 90**

The relationship among all sides of special right triangle

$30° - 60° - 90°$ is provided in this triangle:

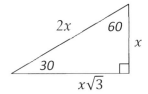

In this triangle, the opposite side of $30°$ angle is half of the hypotenuse.

Draw the shape of this question.

The latter is the hypotenuse. Therefore, the latter is 90 feet.

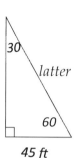

**30) The answer is 2**

Let $x$ be the length of an edge of cube, then the volume of a cube is:   $V = x^3$

The surface area of cube is:   $SA = 6x^2$

The volume of cube A is $\frac{1}{3}$ of its surface area. Then:

$x^3 = \frac{6x^2}{3} \rightarrow x^3 = 2x^2$, divide both side of the equation by $x^2$. Then:

$$\frac{x^3}{x^2} = \frac{3x^2}{x^2} \rightarrow x = 2$$

**31) The answer is 5**

$3x + 6y = \frac{-3y^2+15}{x}$, Multiply both sides by $x$.

$x \times (3x + 6y) = x \times \left(\dfrac{-3y^2 + 15}{x}\right) \rightarrow 3x^2 + 6xy = -3y^2 + 15$

$\rightarrow 3x^2 + 6xy + 3y^2 = 15 \rightarrow 3 \times (x^2 + 2xy + y^2) = 15 \rightarrow x^2 + 2xy + y^2 = \dfrac{15}{3}$

$x^2 + 2xy + y^2 = (x + y)^2$, Then:

$\rightarrow (x + y)^2 = 5$

# PSAT Math Practice Tests

# Explanations

## PSAT Math Practice Test 2

## Section 1 – No Calculator

**1) Choice A is correct**

$5x - 8 = 4.5 \rightarrow 5x = 4.5 + 8 = 12.5 \rightarrow x = \frac{12.5}{3} = 2.5$

Then; $3x + 3 = 3(2.5) + 3 = 7.5 + 3 = 10.5$

**2) Choice B is correct**

$f(x) = x^2 + 2x - 5$

$f(3t^2) = (3t^2)^2 + 2(3t^2) - 5 = 9t^4 + 6t^2 - 5$

**3) Choice D is correct**

$xp + 2yq = 26 \rightarrow xp = 26 - 2yq$   (1)

$xp + yq = 17$         (2)

(1) in (2) $\rightarrow 26 - 2yq + yq = 17 \rightarrow 26 - yq = 17 \rightarrow yq = 26 - 17 = 9$

**4) Choice D is correct**

Let $x$ be all expenses, then $\frac{22}{100}x = \$660 \rightarrow x = \frac{100 \times \$660}{22} = \$3,000$

He spent for his rent: $\frac{27}{100} \times \$3{,}000 = \$810$

**5)  Choice A is correct**

$12x^2 + n = a(x^2 + 3)(x^2 - 3) = ax^4 - 9a \rightarrow a = 12$   And  $n = -9a = -9 \times 12 = -108$

**6)  Choice C is correct**

$\frac{1}{8} = 0.125 \rightarrow C = 5$

$\frac{1}{20} = 0.05 \rightarrow D = 5 \rightarrow C \times D = 5 \times 5 = 25$

**7)  Choice C is correct**

$y$ is the intersection of the three circles. Therefore, it must be odd (from circle A), negative (from circle B), and multiple of 5 (from circle C).

From the options, only $-5$ is odd, negative and multiple of 5.

**8)  Choice D is correct**

let $x$ be total number of cards in the box, then number of red cards is: $x - 246$

The probability of choosing a red card is one third. Then:

$$probability = \frac{1}{3} = \frac{x - 132}{x}$$

Use cross multiplication to solve for $x$.

$x \times 1 = 3(x - 246) \rightarrow x = 3x - 738 \rightarrow 2x = 738 \rightarrow x = 369$

**9)  Choice C is correct**

Plug in the values of x in each equation and check.

   I.   $(-2)^2 - 2 + 6 = 4 - 2 + 6 = 8 \neq 0$

       $(3)^2 - 3 + 6 = 3 - 3 + 6 = 12 \neq 0$

II. $2(-2)^2 - 2(-2) = 8 + 4 = 12 \rightarrow 12 = 12$

$2(3)^2 - 2(3) = 18 - 6 = 12 \rightarrow 12 = 12$

III. $5(-2)^2 - 5(-2) - 30 = 20 + 10 - 30 = 0$

$5(3)^2 - 5(3) - 30 = 45 - 15 - 30 = 0$

Equations II and III are correct.

**10) Choice C is correct**

Let P be circumference of circle A, then; $2\pi r_A = 18\pi \rightarrow r_A = 9$

$r_A = 3r_B \rightarrow r_B = \frac{9}{3} = 3 \rightarrow$ Area of circle B is; $\quad \pi r_B^2 = 9\pi$

**11) Choice B is correct**

Number of biology book: 35

Total number of books; $35 + 95 + 80 = 210$

the ratio of the number of biology books to the total number of books is: $\frac{35}{210} = \frac{1}{6}$

**12) Choice B is correct**

$\alpha = 180° - 112° = 68°$

$\beta = 180° - 135° = 45°$

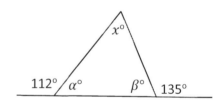

$x + \alpha + \beta = 180° \rightarrow x = 180° - 68° - 45° = 67°$

**13) Choice D is correct**

A. $f(x) = x^2 - 5$     if     $x = 1 \rightarrow f(1) = (1)^2 - 5 = 1 - 5 = -4 \neq 5$

B. $f(x) = x^2 - 1$     if     $x = 1 \rightarrow f(1) = (1)^2 - 1 = 1 - 1 = 0 \neq 5$

C. $f(x) = \sqrt{x + 2}$     if     $x = 1 \rightarrow f(1) = \sqrt{1 + 2} = \sqrt{3} \neq 5$

D. $f(x) = \sqrt{x} + 4$     if     $x = 1 \rightarrow f(1) = \sqrt{1} + 4 = 5$

Choice D is correct.

## 14) The answer is 150

Let $b$ be the amount of time Alec can do the job, then,

$$\frac{1}{a} + \frac{1}{b} = \frac{1}{100} \rightarrow \frac{1}{300} + \frac{1}{b} = \frac{1}{100} \rightarrow \frac{1}{b} = \frac{1}{100} - \frac{1}{300} = \frac{2}{300} = \frac{1}{150}$$

Then: $b = 150$ minutes

## 15) The answer is 66

In the equilateral triangle if $x$ is length of one side of triangle, then the perimeter of the triangle is $3x$. Then $3x = 33 \rightarrow x = 11$ and radius of the circle is: $x = 11$

Then, the perimeter of the circle is: $2\pi r = 2\pi(11) = 22\pi$

$$\pi = 3 \rightarrow 22\pi = 22 \times 3 = 66$$

## 16) The answer is 472

$$\frac{12}{100}x = 72 \rightarrow x = \frac{72 \times 100}{12} = 600$$

$$\frac{1}{8}y = 16 \rightarrow y = 8 \times 16 = 128$$

$$\rightarrow x - y = 600 - 128 = 472$$

## 17) The answer is 3.5 or $3\frac{1}{2}$

One degree equals $\frac{\pi}{180}$.

The angle α in radians is equal to the angle α in degrees times π constant divided by 180 degrees. Then:

$$1 \ degree \ = \ \frac{\pi}{180} \rightarrow 630 \ degrees = \frac{630\pi}{180} = 3.5\pi$$

$$3.5\pi = x\pi \rightarrow x = 3.5$$

# Section 2 – Calculator

**1) Choice A is correct**

$$-3a + 5a + 7a = 45 \rightarrow 9a = 45 \rightarrow a = \frac{45}{9} = 5$$

Then; $\frac{3a-2}{2} = \frac{3(5)-2}{2} = \frac{15-2}{2} = 6.5$

**2) Choice C is correct**

All integers from 11 to 19 are: 11, 12, 13, 14, 15, 16, 17, 18, 19

The mean of these integers is: $\frac{11+12+13+14+15+16+17+18+1}{9} = \frac{135}{9} = 15$

**3) Choice A is correct**

$$|-12 - 5| - |-8 + 2| = |-17| - |-6| = 17 - 6 = 11$$

**4) Choice D is correct**

Based on the table provided:

$$g(-2) = g(x = -2) = 3$$

$$g(3) = g(x = 3) = -2$$

$$3g(-2) - 2g(3) = 3(3) - 2(-2) = 9 + 4 = 13$$

**5) Choice B is correct**

let $x$ be the number of gallons of water the container holds when it is full.

Then; $\frac{7}{24}x = 3.5 \rightarrow x = \frac{24 \times 3.5}{7} = 12$

**6) Choice A is correct**

The quadrilateral is a trapezoid. Use the formula of the area of trapezoids.

$$Area = \frac{1}{2}h(b_1 + b_2)$$

You can find the height of the trapezoid by finding the difference of the values of $y$ for the points A and D. (or points B and C)

$h = 8 - 2 = 6$

AB$= \sqrt{(x_1 - x_2)^2 + (y_1 - y_2)^2} = \sqrt{(6-3)^2 + (8-8)^2} = \sqrt{9+0} = 3$

CD$= \sqrt{(x_1 - x_2)^2 + (y_1 - y_2)^2} = \sqrt{(8-2)^2 + (2-2)^2} = \sqrt{36+0} = 6$

Area of the trapezoid is: $\frac{1}{2}h(b_1 + b_2) = \frac{1}{2}(6)(3+6) = 27$

## 7) Choice D is correct

Choose a random number for $a$ and check the options. Let $a$ be equal to 15 which is divisible by 5, then:

A.  $a - 1 = 15 - 1 = 14$ is not divisible by 4

B.  $a + 1 = 15 + 1 = 16$ is divisible by 4

but if $a = 5 \rightarrow a + 1 = 5 + 1 = 6$ is not divisible by 4

C.  $2a = 2 \times 15 = 30$ is not divisible by 4

D.  $2a - 2 = (2 \times 15) - 2 = 28$ is divisible by 4

## 8) Choice C is correct

$(3^a)^b = 81 \rightarrow 3^{ab} = 81$

$81 = 3^4 \rightarrow 3^{ab} = 3^4$

$\rightarrow ab = 4$

## 9) Choice A is correct

First find the number of pants sold in each month.

January: 110, February: 88, March: 90, April: 70, May: 85, June: 65

Check each option provided.

A. January and February,

$$\left(\frac{110-88}{110}\right) \times 100 = \frac{22}{110} \times 100 = 20\%$$

B. February and March, there is an increase from February to March.

C. March and April

$$\left(\frac{90-70}{90}\right) \times 100 = \frac{20}{90} \times 100 = 22.22\%$$

D. April and May: there is an increase from April to May

**10) Choice D is correct**

First, order the number of shirts sold each month:

$$130, 140, 145, 150, 160, 170$$

median is: $\dfrac{145+1}{2} = 147.5$

Put the number of shoes sold per month in order:

$$20, 25, 25, 35, 35, 40$$

mean is: $\dfrac{20+25+25+35+35+40}{6} = \dfrac{180}{6} = 30$

**11) Choice D is correct**

The ratio of number of pants to number of shoes in May equals $\frac{85}{25}$. Five-seventeenth of this ratio is $\left(\frac{5}{17}\right)\left(\frac{85}{25}\right)$. Now, Let $x$ be the number of shoes needed to be added in April.

$$\frac{70}{20+x} = \left(\frac{5}{17}\right)\left(\frac{85}{25}\right) \rightarrow \frac{70}{20+x} = \frac{425}{425} = 1 \rightarrow 70 = 20+x \rightarrow x = 50$$

**12) Choice C is correct**

The value of $y$ in the $x$-intercept of a line is zero. Then:

$y = 0 \rightarrow 2x - 2(0) = 5 \rightarrow 2x = 5 \rightarrow x = \dfrac{5}{2}$

then, $x$-intercept of the line is $\dfrac{5}{2}$

**13) Choice A is correct**

The sum of the lengths of any two sides of triangle is greater than the length of the third side, therefore the greatest possible value of the biggest side equal to 4 cm. $4 < 6$

**14) Choice B is correct**

$(x - 2)^3 = 27 \rightarrow$ Find the third root of both sides. Then:

$x - 2 = 3 \rightarrow x = 5$

$\rightarrow (x - 4)(x - 3) = (5 - 4)(5 - 3) = (1)(2) = 2$

**15) Choice B is correct**

Number of Mathematics book:        $0.3 \times 840 = 252$

Number of English book:        $0.15 \times 840 = 126$

Product of number of Mathematics and number of English books:   $252 \times 126 = 31,752$

**16) Choice D is correct**

The angle $\alpha$ is: $0.3 \times 360 = 108°$

The angle $\beta$ is: $0.15 \times 360 = 54°$

**17) Choice B is correct**

According to the chart, 50% of the books are in the Mathematics and Chemistry sections.

Therefore, there are 420 books in these two sections.

$0.50 \times 840 = 420$

$\gamma + \alpha = 420$, and $\gamma = \dfrac{2}{5}\alpha$

Replace $\gamma$ by $\dfrac{2}{5}\alpha$ in the first equation.

$$\gamma + \alpha = 420 \rightarrow \frac{2}{5}\alpha + \alpha = 420 \rightarrow \frac{7}{5}\alpha = 420 \rightarrow multiply \; both \; sides \; by \; \frac{5}{7}$$

$$\left(\frac{5}{7}\right)\frac{7}{5}\alpha = 420 \times \left(\frac{5}{7}\right) \rightarrow \alpha = \frac{420 \times 5}{7} = 300$$

$$\alpha = 300 \rightarrow \gamma = \frac{2}{5}\alpha \rightarrow \gamma = \frac{2}{5} \times 300 = 120$$

There are 120 books in the Chemistry section.

### 18) Choice A is correct

Let $x$ be the number of years. Therefore, \$2,000 per year equals $2,000x$.

Starting from \$24,000 annual salary means you should add that amount to $2,000x$.

Income more than that is:

$$I > 2,000\,x + 24,000$$

### 19) Choice C is correct

The amount of money for $x$ bookshelf is:  $100x$

Then, the total cost of all bookshelves is equal to:  $100x + 800$

The total cost, in dollar, per bookshelf is: $\frac{Total \; cost}{number \; of \; items} = \frac{100x+800}{x}$

### 20) Choice C is correct

$\sqrt{x} = 4 \rightarrow x = 16$

then; $\sqrt{x} - 7 = \sqrt{16} - 7 = 4 - 7 = -3$ and $\sqrt{x-7} = \sqrt{16-7} = \sqrt{9} = 3$

Then: $\left(\sqrt{x-7}\right) + \left(\sqrt{x} - 7\right) = 3 + (-3) = 0$

### 21) Choice B is correct

The angles on a straight line add up to 180 degrees. Then:

$x + 25 + y + 2x + y = 180$

Then, $3x + 2y = 180 - 25 \rightarrow 3(35) + 2y = 155$

$\rightarrow 2y = 155 - 105 = 50 \rightarrow y = 25$

### 22) Choice B is correct

The distance of A to B on the coordinate plane is: $\sqrt{(x_1 - x_2)^2 + (y_1 - y_2)^2} =$

$\sqrt{(10 - 4)^2 + (11 - 3)^2} = \sqrt{6^2 + 8^2}$

$= \sqrt{36 + 64} = \sqrt{100} = 10$

The diameter of the circle is 10 and the radius of the circle is 5. Then: the circumference of the

circle is: $2\pi r = 2\pi(5) = 10\pi$

### 23) Choice C is correct

Square root of 16 is $\sqrt{16} = 4 < 6$

Square root of 25 is $\sqrt{25} = 5 < 6$

Square root of 37 is $\sqrt{37} - \sqrt{36 + 1} > \sqrt{36} = 6$

Square root of 49 is $\sqrt{49} = 7 > 6$

Since, $\sqrt{37} < \sqrt{49}$, then the answer is C.

### 24) Choice C is correct

The area of the trapezoid is:

$$Area = \frac{1}{2}h(b_1 + b_2) = \frac{1}{2}(x)(13 + 8) = 126$$

$$\rightarrow 10.5x = 126 \rightarrow x = 12$$

$$y = \sqrt{5^2 + 12^2} = \sqrt{25 + 144} = \sqrt{169} = 13$$

The perimeter of the trapezoid is:   $12 + 13 + 8 + 13 = 46$

**25) Choice A is correct**

$$|x - 2| \geq 3$$

Then:

$x - 2 \geq 3 \rightarrow x \geq 3 + 2 \rightarrow x \geq 5$

Or

$x - 2 \leq -3 \rightarrow x \leq -3 + 2 \rightarrow x \leq -1$

Then, the solution is:  $x \geq 5 \ \cup \ x \leq -1$

**26) Choice B is correct**

Since, E is the midpoint of AB, then the area of all triangles DAE, DEF, CFE and CBE are equal.

Let $x$ be the area of one of the triangle, Then: $4x = 100 \rightarrow x = 25$

The area of DEC $= 2x = 2(25) = 50$

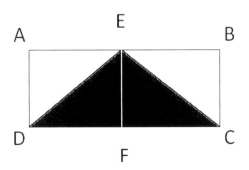

**27) Choice A is correct**

$13 < -3x - 2 < 22 \rightarrow$ Add 2 to all sides.

$13 + 2 < -3x - 2 + 2 < 22 + 2$

$\rightarrow 15 < -3x < 24 \rightarrow$ Divide all sides by $-3$. (Remember that when you divide all sides of an inequality by a negative number, the inequality sing will be swapped. $<$ becomes $>$)

$$\frac{15}{-3} > \frac{-3x}{-3} > \frac{24}{-3}$$

$$-8 < x < -5$$

**28) The answer is 6.93**

Based on triangle similarity theorem: $\frac{a}{a+b} = \frac{c}{3} \rightarrow c = \frac{3a}{a+b} = \frac{3\sqrt{3}}{3\sqrt{3}} = 1 \rightarrow$ area of the shaded

region is: $\left(\frac{c+3}{2}\right)(b) = 4\sqrt{3}$

Round $4\sqrt{3}$ to the nearest hundredths place gives 6.93.

**29) The answer is 0.94**

$$\sin(A) = \frac{opposite}{hypotenuse} = \frac{1}{3} \Rightarrow$$ We have the following triangle, then:

$$c = \sqrt{3^2 - 1^2} = \sqrt{9 - 1} = \sqrt{8}$$

$$\cos(A) = \frac{\sqrt{8}}{3}$$

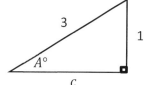

Rounding the answer to the nearest hundredths, gives 0.94

**30) The answer is 80**

One liter=1000 cm$^3$$\rightarrow$ 6 liters $= 6,000$ cm$^3$

$$6,000 = 15 \times 5 \times h \rightarrow h = \frac{6,000}{75} = 80 \text{ cm}$$

**31) The answer is 12**

Based on corresponding members of each matrix, write two equations:

$$\begin{cases} 2x = x + 3y - 5 \\ 4x = 2y - 10 \end{cases} \rightarrow \begin{cases} x - 3y = -5 \\ 4x - 2y = 10 \end{cases}$$    Multiply first equation by $(-4)$, then

$$\begin{cases} -4x + 12y = 20 \\ 4x - 2y = 10 \end{cases}$$    Add two equations:

$$\rightarrow 10y = 30 \rightarrow y = 3 \rightarrow x = 4 \rightarrow x \times y = 12$$

## "Effortless Math" Publications

Effortless Math authors' team strives to prepare and publish the best quality Mathematics learning resources to make learning Math easier for all. We hope that our publications help you or your student Math in an effective way.

We all in Effortless Math wish you good luck and successful studies!

Effortless Math Authors

# www.EffortlessMath.com

... So Much More Online!

✓ FREE Math lessons

✓ More Math learning books!

✓ Mathematics Worksheets

✓ Online Math Tutors

**Need a PDF version of this book?**

Visit www.EffortlessMath.com

Or send email to: info@EffortlessMath.com

38723600R00153

Made in the USA
San Bernardino, CA
13 June 2019